PURPLE
LIGHTS

EDITED BY LEONE ROSS

fp FINCHAM PRESS

First published August 2016. Second edition September 2016.
Published by Fincham Press
        University of Roehampton
        Department of English and Creative Writing
        80 Roehampton Lane
        London SW15 5PH, UK

Design by Rudolf Ammann
Typeset in Calluna and Calluna Sans
Printed and bound by printondemand-worldwide.com
Printed in England

British Library Cataloguing in Publication Data
A catalogue record for this book is available from
the British Library.

ISBN 978-0-9928581-3-1

1. Creative writing; 2. University press; 3. Fiction; 4. Poetry; 5. Nonfiction;
6. Screenplays

CONTENTS

Creative Nonfiction

Screenplays

Novel Extracts

FOREWORD

With *Purple Lights*, Fincham Press is delighted to publish a third anthology of student work, coming after *The Trouble With Parallel Universes* (2014) and *Screams & Silences* (2015). All three editions are available via the university e-store and Amazon, and we encourage you to take a look.

The Press is part of a much larger shift in which universities are becoming once again a site of innovation in publishing, using new formats and channels. The anthologies serve our students, and their contribution enriches the Press and its host, the Department of English and Creative Writing at the University of Roehampton. In addition to this series, Fincham Press is launching a student-run postgraduate journal on behalf of the department, called *Roundtable*.

A technical note: longer stories start on the right only, while short items start on both left and right. Screenplay formatting has been adapted from industry norms to fit the book's dimensions and typeface.

A big thanks to all those who helped make this third anthology possible, with a special nod to our smart and sharp-eyed intern, Charlotte Byrne; designer Rudolf Ammann, our screenwriting leader Elizabeth Clegg, and our head of department, Laura Peters.

Dustin Frazier Wood, editorial board member
Susan L Greenberg, publisher
Jeff Hilson, poetry editor
Leone Ross, anthology editor

INTRODUCTION

Leone Ross

'Where do you get your ideas from?'

It's a common question writers get asked by the public; asked so constantly that many of us roll our eyes and laugh uncomfortably when we hear it. Most of us don't want to try to answer the question in one snappy paragraph or less, but we give it a go, because someone has been nice enough to be interested. Or we react like one novelist who-will-remain-nameless, sitting next to me in 2007: 'Out of my arse, where do you think?'

Oh dear.

As a writer, I'm not entirely sure why the public asks this question so very much. Is it because they think there is some kind of magic repository, or some kind of special finite skill that we can communicate, or some kind of secret that we can explain? Or is it just something you ask a writer, when the room has gone quiet at the start of the Q&A? Perhaps it's the literary equivalent of 'nice weather we're having'. Perhaps the audience don't really care about the answer. But why are we often so uncomfortable, trying to respond?

As Stephen King once said of the question: it's not the point. I think I agree.

Whisper: I don't believe 'ideas' are the secret to writing.

More on that in a minute.

Readers aren't the only ones concerned with this question of genesis. Undergraduate writing students often arrive at Roehampton obsessed with the getting and keeping and care of ideas, the quality and originality of their ideas, what ideas are 'allowed' or 'appropriate' now that they are In University, and in some cases a fear that their ideas will be stolen ('How does copyright work?' this kind of student asks anxiously, plucking at my sleeve. I want to say, 'Nobody is yet interested in your raggedy-ass underdeveloped ideas my love, be concerned with writing something good first...' but I always restrain myself).

Some of our students are even arrogant about their ideas, as if they think them viable simply because they occurred to them: relying on the potency of their own feelings, but balking at the skills necessary to express that passion. 'But it happened to me!' they say. Yes. But you must write it well, too, we insist.

On the other end of the spectrum, many more of our students have to learn to believe in their own ideas, to trust their own wisdom, rather than anxiously write about the things that they have deemed 'literary' prior to their arrival. This lack of confidence can be exacerbated by limited reading or inexperience with a wide variety of writing types. We don't forget the time our poet-editor, Jeff Hilson, shared some of his experimental work during Fresher Week, prompting the departure of one outraged student, sputtering that it 'wasn't poetry'.

Sometimes our students speak of their 'real work', referring to the writing they do outside of the classroom, usually something very close to their hearts, and often including ideas they have deemed unsuitable for the classroom, without ever asking. These are the ideas we usually want to see the most, because they are imbued with authenticity and passion. 'But I didn't think that you would want to read about my made up world/sea monsters/vampire lesbians/life as a working class North Londoner/fan fiction/personal blog/life as a girl/life as a boy,' they say, when we ask to see their 'real' ideas. They regard us with suspicion when we say they should write creatively in their own languages: that they should use the slang, the internet emojis, the patois – the 'imperfect' English in which they are fluent – to write poems or make stories or screenplays, that their 'real lives' are fertile opportunities and they needn't jump out of helicopters before they share. That we are far less concerned about what they write (bar the very occasional intense discussion about particularly racist, sexist, violent or explicit material over the years) and more concerned about how they do it.

But they learn.

You will know this if you've been reading the work of our student writers and alumni over the years. This, our third student anthology, *Purple Lights* includes: explicit sexuality, swearing, madness, fragments of the apocalypse (people love writing about the end of the world), cannibalism, decapitation, the fine art of serial killing (yes, they like that too), monsters in the closet and a very troubling clown. It also includes a most tender treatise on old age, a story about parents lost to tragedy that always makes me tearful, sibling love, and one novel excerpt so sweet and sad it feels like I am inside an old watercolour painting.

There are several virtual hymns to fathers (we seemed to get all fathers this year – it must be something in the water) as well as the titular story that stars a father so worthless that I want to hit him every time I read it. There's prose that is really difficult to read and poetry that is really easy. Oh, and a skinhead, doing stuff you would not expect a stereotypical skinhead to do on a summery day.

So if it's not the idea you need to be asking writers about, what is it? What is the question, if you want to understand the writerly process? If you'd really like to plumb our souls? Or you feel like one of us and want to join the club? There are so many questions. But this is one: ask us about form. About the shape of the thing.

Here at Roehampton, we are a tad concerned with form and structure. A tad obsessed. So this year, we decided to organise *Purple Lights* into sections according to form.

Since introducing our student body to 'flash' forms in the first year, we have had a bumper crop of them, so there are plenty of 'bits' (50 to 950 words for the fiction and nonfiction pieces, 15- to 30-second screenplays) for your reading pleasure. Add that to the experimental poetry – one of the most unique forms we have consistently championed and published – and you can think of all the smaller works in this collection as a platter of *amuse bouche*, or little pieces of jewellery to be browsed. Then we have the longer work (1,000 to 4,000 words) in several genres, all united by the writer's ability to sustain reader attention, to sink us into a world, to keep us with them via fascinating characterisation, elegant metaphors and pacing.

So what if you didn't ask the writer where he/she got his ideas from, but how and why they chose the form? Is it a haiku or a sonnet, or is it the deliciously odd rhythmic opportunity of a prose poem? Is it forty thousand, eighty thousand, one thousand, one hundred words long, and how did that help express an idea? Are they shooting 15 seconds of footage or a feature-length film? When they decided to set down their memories, how did they choose between a book, an article on Buzzfeed or a series of well edited tweets? What silhouette did they first imagine? How did the vessel come into being? And how are they working within or playing with the limits and requirements of these structures?

Why does it feel so important for us to discuss form with student writers? More work has been done around the idea of restriction and the way that limits encourage creativity than I can fit/discuss in this space, but in very basic terms it is like when a young kid ignores the toy in the box and goes off to make the box into a plane and then a bird and then an x-ray machine and then a birthing chamber for aliens in the space of 15 minutes – please tell me that kids still do this. Ergo: when faced with limits, the brain actually spews ideas to cope. We see this happen in practice every year, when a young writer suddenly realises that the trick to this writing lark is not to come up with a stupendously original idea That No One Has Heard Of Before (good luck with that one) but to learn what specific forms of writing require.

So if you know that traditional story usually ends in some kind of change or consequence as a result of the events in that story, then you know if you're writing in that form, this kid with his Christmas box has got to end up not quite the same as he was before, whether he gets a lesson about the nature of selfishness when he's mean to his brother about said pressies, or something he refuses to learn about love, around the corner of the garden shed while pretending to morph between worlds in his cardboard time machine.

If it's haiku you're writing, you come to understand that you are looking for a moment of juxtaposition, that you are finding words to express concrete ideas and behaviours rather than abstract notions (hence, the cat is not 'neglected'; we must actually see its stiff body, mouth upwards to the rain).

You learn about the objective art of rhetoric; more specifically, about the explicit structural choices that bad and good men have made in speeches to lead us down certain paths – not by magic, but by repetition and diction and verb choice. You learn how, in some experimental poetic and prose forms, the manipulation of rhythm and sound of language is way more important than it all 'making sense', because life is not so clean and simple and wrapped up tight, and art has the opportunity to express that truth. That flash fiction or tweet series rely on looking at a moment in all its glory for, as the French say, as long as it takes to smoke a cigarette and no more. That whether you're facing the challenge of flash or the challenge of keeping an audience with you for 100,00 words, ideas – as any writer who's ever been foolish enough to tell a non-writer that they are indeed a writer while sitting next to them on an eight-hour flight knows – are ten-a-penny, and it's not the idea, it's what you do with it, what you actually fashion it into that counts.

Hell, whisper it: the form might give birth to the idea.

Happy purple reading.

Leone Ross

FLASH FICTION

TATE AND PAUL
Tess O'Hara

Two twenty-one-year-old men, Tate and Paul, do Tuesday afternoon either side of the Millennium Bridge. Tate is participating in a Pride flash mob on the South Bank, while Paul's *Patisserie Valerie* date with his grandma is gatecrashed by his friends. Tate knows he's exquisite. He doesn't need your validation. Every molecule of his being is art; every carefully tousled hair. Anything he wears – or is yet to wear – transcends mere fashion, each outfit imbued with higher meaning, like minimalist abstract art, but today he's wearing a round-collared shirt and a kilt with Nike socks and daps. Tate doesn't strive. He'd like you to enter his heart and beat with it, but if you don't want to, Tate doesn't give a shit.

Paul has finally found himself. He stands radiant and tall, dressed in a Burberry cloud grey suit and bowler hat. His face is calm. Most recognise him as that wealthy youngster who models part-time, but those closest to him know that underneath the money is an intense spirituality. They nicknamed him Saint at university. You can never see him from afar, entombed as he is by his friends. When you do spot him, it's sudden and overwhelming, his classic good looks appearing out of nowhere, like a smack in the face.

Tate and Paul both wish to be the new London Tourism Office intern. They will interview tomorrow morning.

The interviewer is an American cool guy in his forties called Brad or Chad or Hunter. He wants to hire someone as dynamic, innovative and cool as himself. His office is all white, except for the colours attached to branded objects: Starbucks

Green, Abercrombie & Fitch Red. On two touching white chairs outside, sit Paul (knees together, feet and eyeballs aligned, facing straight forward) and Tate (leg crossed over his lap, foot lingering over Paul's crotch, plaiting his beard).

The first question Bradchadhunter asks is, 'If you were going to erect a new monument in London, what would it be? What would it say to the British public?'

Tate says, 'Okay, I would erect a large, non-functional crane. It would be all covered in glitter and shit, right. It would have little microphones all over it and shout out compliments to passers-by in a posh accent – this guy outside you've got in next – his sexy voice. The crane would make the public fall in *love* with it. Its lack of usefulness would make it desirable, see. It'll ask the public, like, what is beauty? Why is a monument worth looking at? What is art? Next time they see a crane, they won't be like "Oh, that crane is ruining my Instagram of the London landscape," they'll be like, "Fuck, that's a nice crane".'

Paul says, 'I believe every monument is a celebration, and at the root of this is honour. And who do we want to honour with this monument? Christ. Undoubtedly. Always. So my proposition is – I mean, clearly, not a lot of time to consider – but what do you think of an enormous mosaic of Jesus, his entire body, on the floor of Paternoster Square, and his heart is scooped out of the ground and it's as though his heart is a seat that you can sit in. You can literally sit in the heart of the saviour. We all have walked over him, disregarded him, but still he welcomes us into his love.' Paul smiles. 'This might be inappropriate, but I wonder if you might want to rededicate your life to Jesus in this moment.'

Bradchadhunter tells Paul that he is a Pentecostal on fire for the Lord and loves his idea, and he tells Tate that he's one crazy motherfucker. His second question is more ponderous: 'Why should I hire you?'

Tate says, 'The Universe is expanding. Do you want to

expand with it?'

Paul says, 'My life is a commitment to the tradition and well being of this great city.' He forces one flavourless tear from his eye. 'This is my home.'

Bradchadhunter rolls his eyes. 'One final question,' he says. 'What kind of tasks are you excited about doing, within this role?'

'Bruh,' says Tate, 'I'm excited to come up with more crazy-ass ideas and actually put them into process. I'm excited to inspire the rest of the staff here to come up with their own revolutionary ideas and learn to thrive, just from being in my presence.'

Paul says that he's 'excited at the prospect of convincing the public to pay substantial amounts of money, to not just view but *experience* sites of cultural or sacred distinction, and to make them truly happy about it.'

Both applicants leave confident and wait by the phone, only to be told that some guy called Ben got the job. Ben shared his idea of an oversized Apple watch, stuck to the Houses of Parliament, continuously set to 11:11 – a monument to the First World War, relevant to the current generation.

Apparently, he was also excited to photocopy shit and get Bradchadhunter coffee.

Tate, now an art critic, and Paul, a vicar, cross paths on the bridge one day. They have a brief conversation about the shittiness and atrocity of Ben's idea. They bond and unbond and never speak again.

KICKING BUCKETS
Elisabeth B. Andersen

When I was a little kid, my mother told me not to spook the horses. 'They bite outta both ends,' she said, and I wondered if horses had teeth in the ass. She made me swear.

One morning after milking, once my father and older brother had disappeared out in the cornfields and I could no longer see the tip of their hats, I snuck into the stable.

'It's just me, Sugar Punch,' I whispered and wriggled into the box stall where he stood. Sugar Punch got his name, my dad said, because he was the sugar equivalent of a mean drunk. I didn't know what 'equivalent' meant, and I never asked.

Sugar Punch didn't mind me one way or the other, just flicked his tail and kept on munching his brownish hay. I put the stepladder behind him and climbed onto it, and leaned close to look for teeth. I couldn't see none, just a few clumps of dried muck with some hair stuck in them, so I fig-ured they must be further in. I prodded at his asshole with my index finger.

That really spooked him.

RAIN MAN
Elisabeth B. Andersen

One morning, when Albert is eleven, it starts to rain. The radio and TV immediately report that the schools are closed. All public transport is interrupted. Those who haven't gone out to work yet must stay home; those already there are confined until further notice.

Albert's mother works the night shift at the hospital. Albert's dad went to his office only an hour earlier, when the sky was still metal grey, since Albert's mother would normally be home before Albert heads off to school.

Faced with a morning of doing nothing in particular, Albert stays in bed and leans his chin on the windowsill, nose pressed against the chilled glass. A rose of condensation blooms from where his lips are, but if he holds his breath and then expels it through the corners of his mouth, the window doesn't fog up. That way, he can still look outside.

The rain doesn't so much fall, as it slinks from the sky, slow and sluggish. It makes a sloppy noise whenever it hits something; the ground, the window, the rose bushes in their neighbour's garden. It bubbles against the yellow-dry grass, a muddy blue colour, and washes out all the other colours until everything looks painted and smudged and dingy ultramarine.

When Albert puts a hand on the window, he can feel the vibrating warmth of the rain on the other side.

There is a man outside.

Albert doesn't see him at first; the man, older than Albert's father and with even less hair on his head, has been running from tree to tree, closer and closer, to stay out of the rain. He's wearing a charcoal grey suit that looks too small for him, and his eyes are wild, like a feral cat's.

Albert presses his face more firmly against the window to see, tips it to the side to peer through the blue clots of rain gathered on the other side of the pane. The heat stings his cheeks and forehead where they touch the glass. Finally, the man runs out of trees. He looks around desperately, a small plastic bag in his hand. He clings to it like Albert clings to his teddy bear after a nightmare. The man opens his mouth and yells something, but Albert can't hear it over the slip-slurp of the rain. Nobody comes to help the man.

After staring around himself for a few minutes, looking more and more frightened, the man takes a deep breath. Then he starts running, aiming straight for Albert's house.

'Go, man, go!' Albert says out loud, even if there's nobody else here, and he stands up from the bed so he has a better view. His heart hammers in sympathy with the running man. He probably won't make it, but Albert wishes he would, he really does. The man stumbles in a bloated puddle of rain. For a moment he wavers, arms flailing, and then he drops the plastic bag and falls on his face. Albert cries out in surprise. His palms ache from where he leans them against the window. The man is clearly trying to shout, or scream. He lies in the puddle awkwardly, like he landed on his arm and hurt it, and he's lost one of his shoes.

As Albert watches, the puddle swallows the shoe.

The man tries to rise, using only one of his arms. The other he cradles against his chest, face drawn tight with pain. He manages to get up on all fours. The rain, darkening toward indigo, seeps into his clothes as Albert watches. The man jerks, as if burned, and tries to move closer to the house, but the rain is slowly seeping upwards into his suit jacket and shirt, sliding against gravity like a living thing.

Albert knows he should get back into bed. If his mother were here, she would tell him to shut his eyes, put on some music. She'd maybe hold her hands over his ears so he wouldn't hear the rain, wouldn't hear the distant screaming from outside. But his mother isn't here, and Albert doesn't get back into bed. He watches as the rain slowly pulls the man down into the puddle. Watches as it climbs up his arms, burning the skin to a deep red, swollen colour. Watches as the man's face turns scarlet – first from the force of his screams, then from the raindrops that gather on his face and spread across it. Albert watches strings of rain gather near the man's lips and nostrils. They worm-slide their way in. The man collapses, spasming and bleeding from somewhere Albert can't see, and Albert gets his teddy and holds him tight.

He doesn't get back into bed until the man has stopped moving.

'TWAS BRILLIG

Jessica Lack

Sometimes after school, Daisy and I get home at the same time. It's awkward when it happens. Ambrosia Apartments isn't the kind of place where you get chummy with your neighbours, but Daisy doesn't always get that.

'Hi, Neil,' she says today. She's smiling, so I try not to grimace.

'Hey.' Before she can say anything else, I duck into my dim flat and shut the door. I grab a bag of crisps and sprawl across our ancient sofa. I'm not planning to move for at least an hour.

Then there's a bang and a Daisy-sounding shout from next door. I'm on my feet before I'm conscious of moving. She's a fellow latchkey kid, home alone while her mum does whatever. Picturing burglars, broken windows, and the shifty meth-head from two doors down, I give the wall over the radiator a few hard raps and yell, 'Daisy?'

Another thud, cracking wood, but no response.

Damn it.

I grab my brother's old cricket bat and head outside, hesitating briefly before knocking on her door.

'Daisy? It's Neil. I heard...' Is it weird to bring up how easy it is to eavesdrop on each other? She must know. 'Is everything okay?'

'Sure, it's frabjous,' comes the door-muffled reply. She does that a lot, the made-up words. Who knows what the hell 'frabjous' is supposed to mean.

Before I can ask, something *screeches* inside her flat. The sound startles a flock of pigeons off the roof.

'What was *that*?' I yell.

'The telly!' The words are urgent, and nowhere near believable. I glance around – a couple of gang members on the corner, but they're not interested in me – and pull out my lockpicks.

'Daisy, can you open the door?' There's no answer, apart from splintering wood, so I duck down and set to work on the lock.

I get through in a time that would make my old man proud. I heft up the cricket bat and fling the door open.

I try to swear, but choke on spit.

Daisy is backed up to the door. Beyond her, a *thing* is unfolding itself into the hallway. It's pitch black and angular, and it's got so many jagged teeth, it looks like it's grinning. I'd honestly have preferred the meth-head.

The creature rears back, then launches forward so quickly that my vision blurs around it. I don't have time to lift the bat, or even get out of the way, before it runs past me and disappears into the car park.

Daisy and I stare at each other.

'Well, this is a bloody brangleflust,' she says, and I almost know what she means.

Neil and I reach our next-door-doors at the same time. As I struggle to turn the key in our fickery lock, I study him. Mum and I have lived in this particular flat for three months now, but all I really know about him is that he listens to screamish music that makes my bedroom wall rattle. A girl in study hall said once that he's good with his fingers, but I don't know if she meant it in a sex way or a criminal way.

He notices me watching him, so I smile. 'Hi, Neil.'

'Hey,' he says. And that's it; he disappears into his flat, so I do the same.

I drop my schoolbag and lacrosse gear and start toward the kitchen, wondering if Mum left money for takeaway or if I'll be stuck with leftover casserole for dinner. The *clangk* of the toilet seat falling startles me, and I look down the hall at the closed bathroom door.

'Thought you wouldn't be home yet,' I call. 'Wait'll I tell you about my manxome bloody English instructor's ideas about snarks.'

I expect Mum to scold my swearing perfunctorily, but the only sound from the toilet is a susurrustle of movement and the clatter of something falling on tile.

'Mum? You okay?' I walk up the hall and push open the bathroom door.

The Jabberwock is a surprise.

I only get an impression – oily swoop of a body, pupilless eyes, teeth claws tail *teeth* – before I instinctively slam the door shut. The creature crashes against the other side and the centre bulges toward my face in an out-thrust of splinters.

Mum's the one who knows how to do this. Mum's the one with the vorpal sword. So: get Mum.

I scramble to my bag and retrieve my Deck, fish out two Cards with jitterfast fingers. Eyes on the warping door, I instruct them, 'Find Mum.'

'Don't know any Mum," the Two of Spades sneers.

'She means *Alice*, mimsy dolt,' the Eight of Diamonds hisses. 'What's the message?'

The door screaks, and I wonder if the wood or the hinges will give first. A hysterical giggle jumps out my mouth before I can stop it, because, 'There's a *Jabberwock* in our loo.' The Eight salutes as I slide both Cards under the front door.

I pick up my lacrosse stick and give it an experimental swing: not so much a snicker-snack as a fwoosh-thwap, but better than nothing.

Someone knocks on the front door, and I spin toward the noise, stick raised.

'Daisy?' a voice calls. 'It's Neil. I heard... Is everything okay?' Oh, great. I glance between the front door and the disintegrating loo. 'Sure, it's frabjous,' I lie.

The Jabberwock roars.

'What was *that*?' Neil asks.

'The telly!' I gasp. Where is *Mum*?

Neil says my name again as the creature finally breaks through the toilet door. It grinces, spines of wood caught in its shoulders like quills. I hold the lacrosse stick in front of me, as if it won't be useless.

The door behind me opens. Neil splerks.

The Jabberwock spridles at me, past me, at Neil, *past* Neil, out the door.

Neil stares at me, eyes so wide I can see white all around the brown.

'Well, this is a bloody brangleflust,' I say, and he nods slowly.

A Jabberwock loose in London. Mum is not going to like this.

GABRIEL'S WHARF
Saskia Mears

We came here once, you and I. I was eighteen. Brightly dressed, hair long and soft and decorated with white flowers. I held my shoes in one hand and walked the South Bank with my face turned to the sun; the pavement warm underneath my feet. The colourful doorways and vintage shops accepted me as one of their own and I barely stopped smiling.

You trailed a few steps behind me, huffing about the dangers of going barefoot in London. I wandered from shop to shop, admiring tasseled scarves and badges made out of cotton. You bought pretty buttons embroidered with initials, squirrelling them away for your friends' birthdays. I bought bracelets to cover the scars that hadn't faded. You stopped glancing at my wrists after I put them on.

On the riverbank, I danced, catching bubbles blown by a street performer, and you smiled, but I couldn't see your eyes behind your sunglasses. We poked around a few more shops and started on the food stalls, looking for lunch: you liked salads, I liked chips.

Four years on, the Wharf still looks the same. I can't see the shop that sold the buttons. Pigeons strut up and down the pathways, making the most of pizza crusts snatched from cafes. I stand on the edge of the entrance, my hands shoved as far into the pockets of my coat as I can, tucking my chin into my scarf. I have a duck tattooed over my wrist, now. My hair is shorter. I shiver as the wind plays with it. For a moment I feel nostalgia squeeze my chest, for the teenage girl who never wore matching socks, who had a different flowe for every outfit, who hid sadness in her skin.

The sun filters through clouds and I take a photo to send to you. *Remember this?* Four years on, you have your own scars – from tests, more tests, and surgery. You bought me a single bracelet to wear, to go with the duck. You stopped commenting on my body. *Have fun my lovely* you text back, and I feel warm in the cold breeze. *My lovely. My.*

LAST SUMMER IN SHROPSHIRE
Jack Purkis

During summer, the midday sun makes the cornfields behind my house shine. One evening in late July, I walked across the fields with my friend Alex. The hills looked stitched together, like part of a vast quilt, shimmering through the final hours of daylight in subtle earth tones and deep gold.

The air was hazy and warm; clouds of gnats hung near the trees and bushes. We sat on a wooden stile. The Clun Valley opened up ahead, long shadows stretched down its slopes, grass like the surface of a snooker table. The sun, sinking, gigantic and blazing orange, scorched the cloudless blue sky. I prefer the evenings, the heat is drier, and the wind is soft and cool, like silk. Birds circled above in huge droves; tiny arrows shooting to and fro, finally merging in a large black ball, writhing and convulsing. The light lingered, shades wavering, as if a giant, invisible finger were mixing pastel colours, to create something new.

We talked about the girls at school.

Shag, marry, kill. You go first, said Alex.

I stood on the first rung of the stile, and leaned over to his side. The sun had started to kiss the horizon. It blushed.

Kelsie, I said.

Shoot her?

Yeah.

Thought so.

The ball of birds wheeled high over our heads, all of them screeching. The sound crackled through the air.

Shag?

Emma.

Nice.

I watched the birds fly further away, the noise trailing behind them.

Who would you marry?

Ceri.

Really?

Probably. I mean, she's nice. Super fit.

Yeah, said Alex. He looked down at his shoes.

We carried on walking after Alex complained his arse was numb. The sun had gone, and the landscape drained of its richness. We crossed two more fields, one ploughed, one containing corn. The sky yawned. The final embers of daylight shriveled into the expanding void. It grew cold. Alex picked up a gun-shaped stick and pretended to shoot the sheep on the hillside, now virtually lost to the dark. I saw a piece of sheep shit that looked like a hand grenade and laughed. Alex smiled.

We didn't do me, he said.

What do you mean?

Shag, marry, kill.

OK, who would you?

Kill Kelsie. Shag... Alice, actually.

Marry?

His eyes focused downwards again.

Ceri. I think.

Yeah?

Alex nodded, sniffed, shot a couple more sheep.

Not long after, we decided to head back. We said goodbye at the gate leading to my house. Alex lived a few minutes further down the road. I watched him from the porch, dragging his gun-shaped stick along the ground. At the end of the street he swung it against the tarmac, shattering shards across the road, and threw the remaining piece onto the scattered fragments. I went inside, closed the door, and turned off the porch light.

GLASS JARS

Stiina-Sofia Honkavaara

My mother kept her fears in glass jars, on a shelf above her bed. Whenever I stare at an empty coffee jar, I remember sitting at the foot of my mother's bed as a child, her clammy hands stroking my bald head as I read out the contents of each jar.

'Human hair. Vomit. Dog ears. Needles. Wolf spiders. Moths. Woodlice. Mice. One pipistrelle bat, wings still intact.'

'We must live with our fears,' she whispered. Her voice was as emotionless as her blue eyes.

I stopped myself from asking why no one at school wanted to share my chocolate, and why they all called me Skanky Sue. I didn't understand until a lot later. I had the smell of her on me: a sweet, unpleasant odour. It catches on the back of your mouth, like the viscous grease of a cold meat pie.

It's the same smell in my bedroom, every time I look at my mother, in my glass jars on the shelf above my bed.

JOHNNY
Stiina-Sofia Honkavaara

Whispers about Johnny spread quicker than a snotty cold at Oakfield Primary School. No one knew exactly when Mark and Hamish realised that Johnny believed everything they told him, but they made sure to come up with something new every Monday. It was the talking point through classrooms by afternoon.

Like most Monday mornings, today Johnny had his nose pressed up against the glass of the classroom aquarium, waiting for his first class to start. His eyes followed the tank's latest addition: a slender betta fish with flaming orange fins. Johnny watched it weave between the lush tendrils of hornwort and disappear behind a piece of driftwood.

Above the tank, there was a poster with the words 'Siamese Fighting Fish' written on it and underneath that, 'Comet' in red glitter glue. Hannah had won the name suggestion competition. She was smart like that, Johnny thought.

'You like it?' Hannah's voice came from behind him. Johnny turned his head, letting the frames of his round glasses hiss across the aquarium. She was wearing her hair up in that long, pretty ponytail again. Her hair reminded Johnny of a brown waterfall, or a log, if it was in a ponytail.

'Yeah, I like it! My brother used to have one of these when I was younger. We had to flush her down the toilet when she died, though. Now he has a terrapin instead.'

'Oh cool! What's its name?' Hannah traced the edge of the aquarium with her pink fingernail.

'Pete,' Johnny said. 'I wanted him to call it Michelangelo

or Leonardo, but he didn't. Even Leo would have been a better name.'

Hannah nodded in approval. She must feel the same way too, he thought. He began mimicking what Pete looked like when he chewed bloodworms but his attempts to make Hannah laugh were interrupted by Mark and Hamish's arrival.

'Hey Little Johnny, did you say your brother's got a terrapin?' Mark said. Hamish's freckled face snickered behind him. 'Did you know that terrapins *sing* when you turn them on their backs?'

Hannah shot a disapproving look at Mark and Hamish, but Johnny didn't see it; he was too excited to notice.

'*Really?* I didn't know that! What does it sound like?' Johnny gaped at Mark, who was trying to suppress laughter. Hamish doubled over, smacking his hands against his knees.

'Yeah, I watched it on this nature documentary. It sounds something like this.' Mark squealed so hard and loud that his voice broke and his face turned pink. Hamish laughed even harder and even Hannah looked amused, until she saw that a grim Mr Rogers had entered the classroom.

Mr Rogers ordered everyone to their seats and began his lesson, but all Johnny could think about was Pete, the singing terrapin.

Once Johnny got home, he ran upstairs to his brother's room. He knocked on the door, but there was no answer. Sometimes Alan watched porn with his headset on, so Johnny peered through the keyhole just to be sure. He wasn't on his computer, or lying on his bed, which meant he was out seeing Karen, his newest girlfriend.

Johnny snuck inside and found Pete sunbathing on a log underneath his uv lamp.

'Hi Pete!' Johnny whispered. He wrapped his fingers around Pete's lumpy shell, lifted him out of the tank and put the terrapin onto the parquet floor, on its back. He sat back to watch.

The turtle swayed from side to side, using its head to try to turn itself upright. Johnny squatted closer, urging Pete to sing, but Pete kept pawing at the air until he exhausted himself and opened his mouth. Johnny held his breath, watching the terrapin's small tongue wiggle but there was no sound, apart from a wet puff through Pete's nose and a faint hissing from his throat.

Disappointed, Johnny picked up the terrapin and lifted it to his eye level. The terrapin closed its mouth, and its sides heaved with exhaustion. Poor Pete. Johnny felt bad. He cursed Mark under his breath. He shouldn't have been that stupid, he told himself. Next time he wouldn't believe Mark about anything: like curing his hiccups by snorting cocoa powder or washing his tongue with soap to pass his maths test. He and Hamish just told everyone afterwards and laughed. It was over. Johnny fumed as he settled Pete back onto his log to rest, muttering soothing noises.

That was when Pete opened his mouth again to sing just for him.

FRAGMENTS

Anna Howard

Tucker Walsh
Alabama, USA

It's 1989, and the winter sky hangs heavy over my head. I
reach up to touch it. It feels cold and it scratches my skin.
Something smells thick in the air, like charcoal and gasoline.
I sense everything. My trailer gleams mellow against the
black weather backdrop.

I go sit inside, clutching a bottle of whiskey to my heaving chest. I stretch out and turn the television on with my
big toe. The white static burns my drunken eyes and I kick
the side of the box to get a picture. The news drones on in
its usual dreary way. I scratch my beard and swig from the
bottle, wincing at the taste. Is the newsreader shaking or is
that my vision? I lean forward, trying to focus on the tiny
screen. The ground below me rumbles like a volcano. I fall
off my chair and grasp my head with my hands. The TV falls
on its side and dies. Zap.

Harry and Marina Jackson
London, England

I climb over the wreckage with you in my arms. The sun is
bright in my eyes and I squint. You squeal with rage. I know
you need a bottle but what the hell am I meant to do? I can't
even see a single building still standing. No homes, no
shops, no office blocks. Only a burnt-out green trailer, lying
on its side. I take another step and crunch through shat-

tered glass. You cry harder at the noise and I wince at your tears. 'Shh-shh-shh-shhhh, Daddy's here. Please don't cry.' You're so tiny. Just over a year old. August 17th 1988. You saved us, that summer. I sing to you as I tread carefully over the shards of memory.

Mathilde Dirkse
Amsterdam, The Netherlands

My veins itch. I scratch my skin through my shirt. It's hot. The air is stale and smells like mildew. My mouth is dry, but I can't drink anything or I'll puke. My mattress is stained with dirty sweat and vomit, like expelling my sins through my pores and mouth. The super-flu stage they talk about.

It's been four years since the blast. We're screwed. Amazing how quickly illegal substances creep back into circulation. It's easier to get your hands on a rock than it is a piece of fruit. I traded my last shelter for a week's high. A chance to escape and feel nothing, so who cared about the extra vulnerability? I miss the hit. Sometimes it felt as if my body might forget to breathe, but I always came back to earth. Sometimes I wish I didn't. I could float forever.

I can't keep going on like this, but I can't go back to using, either.

I look out the window. The green trailer glows at me in the dry sunshine. I don't know if anyone has taken it over yet. The girl who lived there before died. Too much junk. I watched her punctured body get hauled out and her stuff looted. That could have been me, left naked in the dust to rot.

I stare at the single yellow tulip standing upright in a plastic bottle on the floor. There's no water in it. It'll die soon. But it pleases me to have a reminder of beauty. Sometimes I shake violently and scream. I'm alone. Who the fuck am I doing this for anyway? No one cares if I use or not. Or die or not. Or lie about it or not. My skin is scabbed from anxious picking and my eyes are sunken and swollen. My pupils: black holes surrounded by puffy skin. Alarm goes off. 11:11. Shoes. No shoelaces.

Wikus Van De Borre and Aneke Botha
Johannesburg, South Africa

I always go back to the room where we began our journey together. We were perfect traveling companions. It is no longer a room but a memory. Where we are now doesn't matter, but where we've been will take over me until I burn out into dust. The trailer that you parked outside my sister's is gone. It's 1991 and I still remember the trailer. It was green and you loved me. The winter grew colder and turned us into constant night. I could smell fear in your bones. We gave in. We shut out what was left of the light in our eyes and walked on, blind. One afternoon, our hands collided and I put the chair in the corner where the radio once stood. I missed music, so I sat there and hummed a tune to the rhythm of your stare. Hey, do you remember? I left you the ring inside the glass bottle. You wouldn't wear it because you said it looked better in the bottle than on your bony finger. And I didn't even mind.

SOHO NIGHTS

Patrick Hawkes

There's a picture by my bed that reminds me of a boy. He isn't in it, but the morning after we first met and not long after we fucked, he picked it up and asked, 'Who's this?' His prints are still smudged across the frame.

I met him in Soho on my birthday. It was past two and I was cold, waiting to get into a club with my friends. The Italians behind us walked off and I was laughing at something but actually feeling lousy that this guy Tony had left, who I'd kind of been seeing. Alice was talking to this boy stood with us, laughing through his green eyes and mouthing off at the Pizza Express round the corner.

We lost him at the door and I bought drinks, danced with Alice. Charlie got talking to this old queen from Hackney so I stepped out for a cigarette, and stood in the street on my phone pretending to text when green-eyes came over and said, 'Hi.' He was stunning. He told me his name was Nathan and we chatted until his friends came out; an annoying Russian and somebody that wanted pancakes.

We found my friends and sat outside Bar Italia, warm under electric lights and safe from the rain under an awning. The street was busy, loud and wet, rickshaws and beggars drifting with the Saturday night crowd. He was on my lap, his head resting against my shoulder and my dick getting hard against his leg, making him laugh. When his friends asked, 'What?' he just kept laughing. He had coffee and I had pizza sauce on my chin where he'd missed, trying to get me to take a bite.

Then running, running through streets: neon and backlit puddles, brick alleys and Somalian dealers; screaming, spinning circles past Piccadilly Circus and street dancers and thugs. Eyeing strange shapes and colours and sounds, purple lights; the damp pavement beneath me as I sat. Buses, passing traffic –

'Where do you live?' he asked.

'South Kensington.'

'Are you rich?'

'Nah, I live in a bedsit.'

His friends left. He kept messing with my hair as we walked, Alice and Charlie a bit ahead. Walking through the subway under Park Lane I told him Alice was a rock star, she'd played Reading and would be very famous. Charlie said she was Swedish and I didn't listen to the rest, out of the tunnel and distracted by lights and headlights and a ringing in my ears I couldn't place.

'Can you hear that?'

'What?'

'That ringing, listen.' I looked up, went 'Hummmmmmm-mmmm.'

'Oh yeah, hummmmmmmmmmmm.'

We climbed over a fence to get into Hyde Park and lay on the pavement, seeing stars. Alice sat rolling cigarettes. He said he worked in a sweet shop and made art, jewellery; studied at Central Saint Martins. When Alice was ready to go we left her and Charlie at a bus stop, walked to mine. I gave him a piggyback through Knightsbridge and he slid off when I stumbled, then pulled me in for a kiss, his breath hot in my face and his taste –

Armpits, balls, heavy breathing; nipples, skin, wet sheets and those eyes. The flush in his cheeks when he came.

WORLDS ON A SHELF

Harriet Maukisch

I loved my grandmother's pantry. When I was little I could hide there for hours. Explore. Taste things and feel their texture. Hard pulses and soft oats. Spikey rice and round letter-shaped noodles. Onions on the windowsill next to the just-laid eggs. The smell of freshly baked cake always lingered in there, the sweet stickiness of melted chocolate mixed in with the tang and tickle of vinegar and soap. But what I loved most were her shelves, hidden behind the door, full of spice jars. Vibrant colours, textures, and shapes, and grandma was their mistress. She knew how to choose the exact turmeric and chilli to make her soup taste full of love and warmth; that cardamom in lemonade cooled you down on a hot summer's day; how to make the worst heartache go away. She could punctuate a curry with fenugreek and ginger as quick as she'd choose spices to cure your heartsickness. She knew their magic.

I was allowed to look, sometimes to touch, never to use them. 'They need respect Tanny,' my grandma said, 'or they will fool you and destroy everything. If you respect them, one day they will call to you.' I did. I spoke to them whenever I was there. I stroked the glass of the jars, I tapped her handwritten labels. I was respectful. I was good. I was also curious. One day, I opened her jar of chilli powder. It was warm, tickling my fingertips and heating the soles of my feet. It was lava, lapping at my legs. Her salt was fresh and wavy, rushing and slushing me around, like a little boat on the big open sea. Her pepper made sandstorms. Big and beautiful and loud. Her lovage sent me to green mountains and the thyme and rosemary drove me through small villages full of fresh baked bread and grilled meat. I loved it. Her spices let me explore and taste and feel.

I got too sure of myself. I troubled the turmeric, handling it without gentleness, hurrying and careless, so it burned me like the sun. Hot and unforgivable, thousands of needles scratched along my skin. My grandmother saved me. She calmed the turmeric with soothing vanilla and lavender and promises of atonement. I said I was sorry and the spices forgave me. Grandma and I never spoke a word about it again. Now, every time I go out into the sun, my skin shimmers orange-golden. Warmth pulses around me.

I'm a mistress of spices, now.

CUP OF COFFEE
Corinna Miller

The only thing I knew for sure about my dad was how he took his coffee in the morning.

The rest of it was pieces of different movie dads, all spliced together in a weird mish-mash of a person. In my mind, dad has the salt and pepper charm of George Clooney in *The Descendants*, the intelligence of Sean Connery in *Indiana Jones*, and the humor of Steve Martin in *Cheaper by the Dozen*. The worst thing to imagine about a guy who's your dad isn't that he's dead in a ditch somewhere – it's that he's happy and successful and busy being the dad of two *other* girls who gladly take twenty dollars from him to go shopping and call him 'daddy' and get away with raiding his liquor cabinet with no more than a slap on the wrist.

I was only about four when he left my mom and me. We didn't fall apart without him, though. We do just fine. Mom works and I go to school. There isn't a weird stepdad who touches me, or some bastard who hits my mom or anything. There's just Glen, her boyfriend. He helps me with my calculus homework and gives me disapproving looks when I disobey my mom. He walks with a limp and she won't tell me why, but he stays over a few times a week and does a bit of cooking when she comes home from work. Mom won't let him move in, even though they've been together for almost three years now, so I think the arrangement works for both of them.

Glen drinks tea.

Dad took one sugar and a cream with his coffee. I remember because he would let me open the little packet of sugar every morning before he went to work. I'd pour about ninety percent of it into the cup before pulling it back and keeping the last ten percent to eat myself. I'd lick my fingers, then open the little pot of cream. That part was my favourite, because of the patterns it made in the coffee. It would be a tiny drop of cream, then suddenly sprout wings and fly through the mug, creating little clouds and flowers along the way. Watch the next time you put cream in your coffee – it's true. Dad let me watch the cream for a minute before he stirred it in, clouds fading into the brown liquid. I always loved how the colour of the coffee lightened. Made it look like milk chocolate, although whenever Dad let me try a sip, I was disappointed it didn't *taste* like chocolate.

The last thing Dad did before putting on his beige trench coat and heading to work was take a nice long sip of the coffee. He'd put the mug up to his lips, breath in the steam, then sip for a few seconds before pulling it away, lick-ing his lips, and humming his approval.

Mom told me my dad died the other day. She didn't say much else, there were no tears or talks about mortality, even Glen barely looked up from his newspaper. I was never a fan of cof-fee, but that morning, I poured myself a cup. I took a small sip and hummed like my dad. I thought I'd feel some sort of connection to him, but there was nothing except the bitter taste of coffee sliding its way down my throat.

'Since when have you liked coffee?' my mom asked. I told her I didn't.

Then I went over and asked Glen how he took his tea.

PARTY

Katherine Armstrong

It's her party and her place and we squeeze through the cat flap and suddenly we're children again: scared of the floor, the mud-stained tables and scratched sofas.

'It's lava! The floor is lava!' screams a boy, balancing on the edge of a coffee table. He thinks his hands are webbed and sticky and capable of gripping the wall. He leaves a dull brown smudge next to a hanging photo frame. A girl writhes and wriggles in one corner of the living room. She's on her back, like a woodlouse. I roll her over and see the bottom section of her nostrils isn't there and remember we're all dissolving in here. Thinning bodies, shadows under our eyes growing, like waning moons.

The game of hot lava (where you can't touch the floor) might have ended, or the party-goers decided to sacrifice themselves to the carpet; they swim towards me and cackle in my ear about icing sugar and funny gas and cough syrup. They know I understand their drugged, intoxicated murmuring. I tell them no, my pockets are empty. I'm emptying the kitchen cupboards – I find tins with those cheap hot dog sausages in – mechanically recovered meat, the bits hanging off the corpse that no one wants. My new acquaintances and I leap over each other, giggling and hungry.

'I once knew this boy, right. And he was properly *wankered* and he had some crap hotdog outside a club and he puked and then. Well. The sausage, it came out whole. It came out whole and he ate it again.'

I'm going to be sick.

'She didn't compliment my dress.' I say this to the wall because the host's not here. She's in a busier room. She loves me but she's scared to be seen with me. Homophobe. She's scared of me. Good. I see the clock she made in woodwork class, Year Nine. I bang my head on the stupid wall and the stupid clock falls to the floor and breaks into two pieces.

Where is she? I'm crawling on all fours again, dragging my tail across the coarse carpet. I tell everyone that yes, it's there, the tail. I need something soft to stroke, to wrap around me. But it's a lot of effort and eventually, I give up. I'm an apologetic note ripped out of an old notebook and slid under the door. I stare at the circling room.

Beige. Everything is beige.

I'm heavy and I hate it.

WORDS
Cleo Wreford

One day I began to see the names of things, hovering like party balloons tied with ribbon: clusters of words written in cramped letters, like anatomy notes.

Sometimes they *are* anatomy notes.

There are a certain number of categories and subcategories within every object – the number varies. The amount I see depends on how close I get to the thing. If I'm far away from a beach, I see *beach*, written above it, as if a note has been tattooed on the sky. As I get closer, I can see what's on the beach, floating about waist-height. *Pebble, pebble, glass, pebble, dead fish*, all overlaid until barely anything is visible any more. It's worse on sandy beaches, obviously.

The day I began to see the words, I opened my eyes to *nightstand, lamp, alarm clock* and a jumble of letters: *wirescondomstissueshairbrushwaterbottle waterspider*. I rolled over, tried to get back to sleep, or awake, because I thought I was dreaming. When my alarm went off I brought my hand down to silence it through a veil of identifiers.

I got ready for work, ignoring the words that hovered over my clothing, telling me of threads and dust and cotton. It was stress, maybe; it was a dream, maybe. It would be fine.

It was not fine.

There is something in the human mind that doesn't like large numbers of things, or rather something in *most* human minds, because there are people out there who do maths about infinity and seem to be fine. Most people, though, when thinking about lots of things, tend to have that feeling which surfaces on long travels on public transport and evenings when you don't know what to do with yourself. A terrifying sense of scale – that there are so many things and more of them than we can even count or imagine. So we put things into compartments. The space between the hedges is a field, which contains an amount of grass, an amount of bugs, an amount of sheep or cows, an amount of things buried or lost amongst it, a sum that adds up to 'I don't want to think about it'.

I left the house, following the words with cautious interest. Above the houses there was *house*, thousands of illegible words clustered beneath, forming a pyramid of letters that got smaller and smaller until it was almost like smoke.

I only turned back when I saw another person.

I get up so early it's still dark, and so on my walk to the bus stop I rarely see other people. That day there was a man, walking a dog, but I couldn't see him. He was a mass of words, and as I grew closer I could see that most of them said 'hair'. The dog was the same, coated with *hairhairhairhairhairhair* all interlocked and overlaying. When you see the human body like that, annotated, it tends to make you anxious.

I went home and looked in the mirror. Then I had a panic attack.

Since then I've gotten better, or just used to it. I can leave the house now, go to work, all the things that I did before. I just do so amongst black blobs instead of people; the only issue I really have is trying to hand things to people. The mist is thick, and I don't know where their hands are sometimes. The same thing with eye contact. Perhaps I just seem a little distracted, but anyone would be if they knew what everyone they met had for lunch or had growing inside them. If I put my face close to someone else's, the words swim about me like a shoal of fish. Hovering over our heads, something like *man*. Or *woman*. Or anything else someone can be. Then there is a layer of general things. *Arm*, it says. *Arm, leg, leg, tomato, bacon, jumper, jeans, blood, stomach*. If the person is wearing it, or has it within them, it'll be there. These words are not as big as the first label, the catch-all, but they are legible. Beneath that, everything is described smaller and smaller, until it's just a haze. They layer the body, each word corresponding to the general anatomical area it covers. Just like that first man, most people, beneath the larger words, are just *hair* for the most part. But I see diseases, too. I see cancers. I once congratulated a woman on the bus about her pregnancy, and she asked how I knew. 'I haven't told anybody, I'm not even showing yet, how can you tell?' I told her that she was glowing. Her voice sounded pleased after that.

A few days ago I was walking from the bus stop to my house, and someone walked past me. Like I said, the words are normal to me now; I'm fine with them, as long as I avoid thinking about them too much. This was different, though, and I turned my head to read as I walked by.

After I read his annotation, I knew I had to follow the man home.

I did it easily – the streets were mostly empty. He didn't live too far away from where we'd passed. I stood back and blinked at the mist of words above the terraced house before going home to get my binoculars. I used to bird-watch, sometimes, when I was younger. I'd go with my grandfather, and he gave me the binoculars three years before he died. I'd kept them on a shelf to gather dust after that.

I went back to the man's house, and I held the binoculars up to my eyes, and then I dropped them. They bounced off the pavement with a thud and a crunch.

Earlier, I'd caught a glance of two words, bobbing around the man's stomach. I'd hoped I was wrong, until I saw the third word above the house.

It hung there, shifting slowly.

Corpse.

Floating beside the man's stomach, I truly had seen the words: *Human. Flesh.*

2345 AD
Sam Rose

In the year 2596, twenty-four-year-old Tom Strion was awarded
Employee of the Year and won a holiday to any destination
he wanted. He considered going to visit his parents but he
thought that would be too upsetting, so instead he chose at
random.

On December 31st, 2596 Tom left in his company's time
machine and arrived on January 1st in the year 2345. He arrived with little to no knowledge of the period, no connections to anything and a few months' savings in his pocket.
He booked himself into a hotel and researched current af-
fairs, so as not to stand out. The world he was in was similar
enough to the one he would return to in a year's time. He
was comfortable.

On his first cold night, he walked around his home town;
only it was 251 years different. He smiled as he strolled past
his school, with six fewer floors and a lot more trees. Things
seemed smaller, quieter, more peaceful. He liked that. Re-
markably, Simpson Heath was the same – the very park where
he'd spent his childhood running around, chasing his
friends and his imagination. His desk job had since separated him from both. After standing a while with the sun
setting behind the lowered skyline, he ran around in circles
until he was out of breath and fell into the snow, giggling.

The following month, Tom turned himself into a man
of the 24th century. He dressed the right way, picked up on
the phrases people turned, and socialised. He went to clubs
and flirted with women who were 251 years older than him
and still got ID'd at the bar. Tom discovered that being from
the future was a turn-on for women so he flaunted it, even

though telling people was illegal. He was careful, though: he didn't give anything important away. He told women just enough to get them into bed: who won the football in a particular year, what music people had started listening to, what they would wear in the future. He kept all the scandals, all the technology and all the important events to himself, just like the guidebook told him.

Tom lived like this until March. He would go to a club and tell enough women he was from the future, until one of them came back to bed with him. Then, next morning he would show them the door. When March came, Tom decided the climate was warm enough to spend the night alone and started to enjoy other aspects of the past. He read the literature, went to see the music and watched the films, but by the time June came, he felt he'd done everything. On the evening of June 21st, he walked up Simpson Heath to Simpson Hill and sat alone and cried. He wept for the time he had wasted sleeping with women who would all be dead in six months. He wished he had gone to see his parents instead. Then he wept for them; they were dead and they hadn't even been born yet.

SARDINES
Charlotte Byrne

I've been ripped off already. You get charged the peak fare if the train is meant to arrive before 10am. Thirty-odd pounds is a bit steep when you have to stand.

I'm standing now. There's a bar pressing into the small of my back, which is starting to twinge. My chin itches where I haven't shaved this morning, or possibly because I'm sweating. A younger man next to me has stupid hair and stupid cologne and a stupid phone, and is leaning into me. I'm conscious of my breakfast breath and trying not to breathe.

There's a girl opposite me, but I can't look at her face. There's an unwritten rule about not making eye contact. I don't know if she's beautiful. Instead I gaze at her legs. She has lovely legs. She's got thin tights on and I wonder she's not cold. Then I think better of what I'm doing and stare at the stupid winkle-picker wanker shoes at eight o'clock. I can't look at girls' legs. I'd be a pervert.

She might be a nice girl. (Stupid laces.) She could be the greatest girl I'd ever know. She could be a waitress, or a tree surgeon. (Stupid socks.) Perhaps she's an assassin, or keeps bandicoots. (Stupid cologne.) She could even be my wife one day. I'll never know. I'm not even allowed to make eye con-tact.

NOT TONIGHT
Charlotte Byrne

I'm waiting and waiting. I can hear the caller mumbling the numbers he really needs to speak up into the mic. What if the old dears can't hear him who knows how much they could be missing out on, sometimes it's grands and other times hundreds. It's all the same really we all go for the thrill of it well that's what I tell meself whenever I hand over me seven quid for me book. Sometimes I have two but I can only do one today only one until me Giro comes through.

Come on Cynth you can do this you can do this you can you only want twenty-two for the house and then you've done it girl you'll be quids in.

'Twenty... one!'

Fucking bollocks teasing little bastard you'll give me heart attack in a minute but nobody's called it so it's okay. You're still in girl gotcha eyes down it'll be all right. Dab it nice and plain but that's no good it's on another bloody card and there's someone sneezing and it must be putting us all off because even the caller's getting all on edge. More numbers but they're no good to me they're all on other cards and everyone must be waiting and it's too much. It's so tense you could cut it with a knife you really could but there's a greasy smell on account of someone's had sausage and chips and all I've got is a cuppa char and if I win I'll get some chips. Mind you what's the likelihood I've been coming thirty year and it always ends the same.

'Twenty... *two!*'

But not tonight.

'Here y'are!' It's me I've done it I've done the fucking lot of yous and here I am leaping up and waving me card around like a woman possessed and the man's coming over to check it and he does it and I've done it and I want to scream and I want to cry. I'm exploding inside all like the fireworks the little twats set off round the estate and all the old dears are tutting and moaning and grumbling like you always get when there's a win. Only normally it's me what's doing it and tonight I've done it and he's coming over with me enve-lope and it's a grand and it's chips in a minute and you know what I might even fuck off to Malia as well.

RIDLEY ROAD

Steph Elliot Vickers

Tariq has a new job, selling fish on Dalston Market. He un-packs them onto ice with the care of an undertaker as the sun begins its sprawl across the city, careful not to meet their vertebrate eyes. They disturb him.

He thinks of halal slaughterhouses, how they used to honour each death with an Imam's prayer, fluttering hands, until there became too many; he thinks of all the animals whose prayer was pre-recorded. The perversion is salty on his tongue, but everything is: every apron, knife and surface glistens slick with salt water, but nothing can rinse the death smell from his nostrils or fingernails. He whispers a prayer to each fish before ripping its insides out through its gills. Pages from yesterday's *Metro* dance around his ankles. An elderly street cleaner with a face of folded silk sweeps them away.

Tariq says sorry a lot. Says it so much it starts to bleach his integrity. Says it until he realises, marinating in fish guts and November wind chill, that for as long as his boss deter-mines his worth at £3 an hour, he owes nobody 'sorry' – es-pecially not him – not the friends he can't afford to see, the fish he didn't kill, nor the customers who snap at him to hurry up, and can he not scale a salmon faster than this? Tariq stops apologising and praying and says nothing, and the cold days pass in blood and silence.

He starts playing a game of liberties that helps him put up with the piss-poor working conditions and piss-pooled Ridley Road. His favourite: taking gradually lengthier smoke breaks with the Rasta record shop owner, five stalls down.

He is the only person Tariq can talk to without shame.

'It's my boss. He cheats everyone.' He spits, sounding like one of the Rastaman's overplayed records, inhaling smoke and guilt. 'He makes me cheat everyone.'

The man's locks sway when he shakes his head.

'I couldn't wuk fi a dog like him; only care 'bout money. Mek yuh feel dirty like him. But yuh is not him, yute. Work honest, an' keep yuh pride. What else yuh have?'

Tariq smiles, stubs his cigarette out with his shoe, and wanders back to work. He picks out sea bass for a pointing man with weathered skin and kind eyes: three for £5. He can feel his boss's breath on the skin of his shoulder.

'Don't give him all the biggest ones,' the boss warns in Punjabi.

Tariq is torn; he hates his mother tongue used to talk about people in front of them, and each time he hands over under-weighed, over-priced goods he feels like an accomplice to his boss's greed. When the kind-eyed man picks the biggest bass, Tariq obeys him, shielding the fish in his apron so the boss can't see their quality and weight. He scales them perfect, cuts them uniform, bags them tight and hands them over with a smile; his first genuine smile since starting at the stall. His chest warms with something other than nicotine: pride, he realises. He likes working honest.

The customer he's taken so much care to serve tears the bag open, and peers inside. 'What are you playing at?' he snaps. His eyes are plugholes. 'You've swapped my fish out. You've swapped them for *smaller* fish!'

'W-what?' Tariq stutters. The sound of his voice sickens him. 'But you stood and watched me! You *saw* them. You –'

'You swapped his fish?' A waiting woman pries, looking up from the display. A street sweeper shifts his weight to the broom and his eyes to Tariq, who feels the very tarpaulin of the stall folding in on him.

He tries to gulp down his rising anger but it's already

spilled over his tongue, until he's drowned the man in so much of it that all he can do is back away, horrified at himself and the words he's saying. He takes off his fish apron and drops it on the wet ground and looks at the fish eyes and the eyes of the man he's cursed, turns his back to all of them, and walks away. Is this worse than being fired?

Tariq's boss watches him go. He doesn't yell after him, or complain.

Tariq can hear him laughing.

THE SMALL THINGS

Nika Cobbett

Looking right and left was never one of the skills he'd been able to list on his LinkedIn page; listening to the roar of a screaming American truck not something he practised often; road safety a vague concept they made cartoons about, with hedgehogs for children. So as he came to be, lying on the motorway, staring at a dull navy blanket of a sky, he didn't think twice about that twinkling monstrosity tootling down the deserted motorway at 3:43 in the morning. Dil didn't think to haul his tricked-out arse from where he was lying in the left hand lane. The blue and red carnival lights swirled, in oncoming, incomprehensible patterns, curling over each other and leaving all the fun of the fair on the hard shoulder.

Dil was much too high and he attributed this to the cocktail he'd snorted and shot and licked and rolled in; visions were the goal. He needed visions for his art; the world couldn't give him transcendence and a stairway to the right hand of glory like it did when he was fifteen, but come to think of it he'd been high, then, too. And to work in an office was to die, his dad always said.

Much too high, he kept thinking, over and over; he was much too high.

The sky wasn't up any more, the sky was under him and looking up; he saw himself. Bits of himself scattered and splattered and my god this was one hell of a vision, a hallucination and all of a sudden he was Jesus in the air, and it all started to make sense. He was looking at his arm over there – it was definitely his because it had that backyard tattoo on his wrist, an infinity loop. He was going to get his friend to tattoo him an ouroboros snake but then he read that book where they said the word ouroboros about fifty times and he wanted to throw the word in a lake and set fire to it.

All of a sudden he had this terrible nostalgia for solid things under solid feet, and he found he was floating in a way he didn't quite approve of, in a way that would make coming down very painful indeed. And he thought of how clear the night was, it had no right to be this clear when he'd spent good money to make it skew on a morbid and colourful axis. Death rolled in waves off the floor and he floated a few inches higher, instead of staggering like you're supposed to do when the smell and sight of decay hits.

Was that his leg? It had a kind of familiar shape. Oh look, it was his leg. Still connected to a body. Convenient, he thought, for the police to clean up.

He'd wanted to be a police officer, he recalled; mounted unit was where he focused all his attention. Only, he never learned to ride an actual horse so the police kept saying no, and besides, he kept getting arrested.

Floating in the air offered him an unequalled view of a singularly boring motorway; the tootling truck had long since sped off in one direction or another and now all he had to study were his body parts and it was getting old. Art College got old too; too many deadlines, not enough hedonism. Head, where's the head. There's his head, it still has a torso covered in bits of old charity shop jumper.

He used to wear those tarpaulin jumpers, stretched tight over expectations, and loose over shrunken stomachs. Cargo pants, hiding the building site underneath. Wouldn't even take them off for that girl in his bedroom; she'd laughed. So they'd smoked a lot, she passed out while he watched Japanese cartoons and she mumbled dangerous words in her sleep. 'I love you' it came back to him like that. He could hear her snuffling and mumbling. 'Don't let the rhinoceros win.' That made him laugh hard, holding himself tight and silent and heaving from within; he didn't want her waking and repeating her dangerous words into impressionable pillows.

He could see the motorway getting closer again; the stars winked their goodbyes and policemen turned up with ambulances in tow. He watched them all shake their heads in turn and pull out their white sheets, four of them. A policeman sticking his arm under sheet number one with eyes squeezed shut, groping until he pulled out a wallet and phone. His wallet. Dil croaked indignantly. Then panicked, thinking of the not-very-well-hidden leftovers from last night's score. Then it occurred to him there were no leftovers, there never were and it was a well known issue among his friends but one he'd never figured out how to fix.

He sank yet further and drifted over to the policeman who'd been digging in his pockets; he had his phone in hand, screen cracked and contacts open on 'Mum.' That was a killer, his mum with her pinched little face, sucking on disappointment as he rolled in the door. Shouldn't this be ending soon? Any minute now; any minute now and he'd wake up in some daft place, with people he didn't remember and smells he couldn't handle. He'd throw up into the bushes and rave about the days of the dying sun. Any minute now.

SHORT STORIES

PURPLE LIGHTS
Katherine Gutierrez

I take the 457 bus every day after school, choosing a seat near the back and looking out of the window at the grey, windswept Henrikson Boulevard that is perpetually stuck in the dead of winter, flattened *News Underground* papers stuck to the sidewalk.

The 457 goes through a tunnel on the way to Kilmer Avenue. The tunnel is lit with purple lights that shoot through the aisle, illuminating the scattered shadows of people and myself. I lean my head back against the headrest and I wish the lights could stay with us and that we could travel down that tunnel the whole ride.

There is a man who always sits in the front priority seat. He's what my mother would call a 'no-good 'n'. He looks very old, his skin reminds me of the cracked, black leather of old men's shoes and he has a felt brown hat that he wears pulled down. He comes alive when I exit the bus, looks at me with his filmy eyes and smiles.

'It's gonna be a good day!' he says and cackles, shaking his head. 'It is gonna be a *good* day-to-day.'

I never reply, I just leave as fast as I can.

I'm not good with things like that. Running into unexpected things, chance encounters. I was once in a Dory's 24-hour diner with Hilary at two in the morning, keeping her company when she got locked out of the house for the night. We drank coffee with free sweetened milk because that's all we had money for and she talked about the bullshit of capitalism for a while. She's very keen on the bullshit of capitalism. She has Che Guevara posters on her walls and she smokes weed instead of attending Phys Ed because it's what the Communist Brotherhood would have wanted.

A small group of Hare Krishnas came in from the streets, their orange robes and shaven heads overly bright in the florescent lighting. They befriended Hilary and shared their barbecue chicken wings with us. Hilary had in-depth discussions on philosophy and education with them, until the sun came up. They invited her to a meeting at one of their temples over on Seventh and Fourth where she apparently just laid flat on the floor as they burned cinnamon incense and played Radiohead.

I scrunched in the corner and ordered a glass of tap water, leaving for the first train the second the sky turned pale blue. I wish nothing unexpected would ever happen to me, I just end up regretting how I deal with it.

When my bus stops at Hansen I get out and walk the rest of the way. My house is down an alley that hardly anyone in the neighbourhood remembers is there. It used to be part of a main street, a sprawling, affluent area with elms in the front yard and swimming pools in the back. Now no one is allowed to grow trees because of the sudden infestation of brown-back beetles and our road is so forgettable sometimes the piles of trash on the front drives don't get collected for days.

I walk up my drive and see that the kitchen light on the left is on. That means my mother has decided to make dinner and put Amy in front of the TV to watch *Blues Clues*. On evenings when the living room light on the right is on, Amy is locked in her room upstairs and mom is praying. Sometimes she has her prayer group over. I hate coming home to their mess. They're a group of hand-rubbing evangelicals who call themselves the Disciples of Light and they come to remind my mother that only Jesus knows the answers, as they eat all the meatloaf she makes them, sopping our food stamp bread into the gravy. They believe that Judgement

Day is coming sometime soon and my mother hangs saint portraits she buys at the West Water flea market on every wall of our house.

When dad was still here, there was no church group or empty fridges or Virgin Marys with their hands folded, lined up in the hallway. We'd watch *True Crime TV*, eat takeout Chinese and pink sweet bread from the Mexican bakery, go out to mini golf when I got a good grade. There was always expensive wine in the fridge. I remember coming down for a nighttime snack and seeing my parents outlined by the Japanese lamp, clinking glasses.

When I get home I usually peer in at my mother, kneeling on the chequered rug, rubbing the pearly rosary the church group sold her for thirty-seven dollars between her palms and murmuring to herself. She doesn't hear me anymore. Sometimes when I say, 'I'm back!' she looks up vaguely at some space behind me before looking down again.

I go into the kitchen to put some bread in the toaster. I bring a packet of chocolate animal crackers up for Amy. I open the windows in my room and I try to get used to smoking. I've decided to take it up as I have nothing better to do. Hilary lent me some of her Camels, but she rolls hers and I can't be bothered with that. I thought I'd get hooked after the first one, but it's something I could definitely live without. I like the rough, ashy taste at the back of my throat and the smell of tobacco, but mostly the smoke. I like how it looks when I smoke at night. A sinew, curling up. I don't get so hungry when I smoke, I find it easier to think.

At night with only weightless air inside me, I feel pure. Something that's been wrung out, left to dry and is quietly dissolving in the dark.

I feel immensely powerful, planning the ways I could put everything back together. I decide to call my father, put Amy back in daycare, confront my mother's church group. I resolve myself and the next day I pack my schoolbag, eat a spam sandwich and take the 457 bus to school. The truth is, no one is powerful. We are all bullshitters.

The tall, Jewish Spanish teacher who organises my form room asks me every once in a while how things are at home. She has big, watery eyes like a spaniel and I almost blabbed to her once, but she's too twitchy for me to trust. She wears a red scarf all the time and I've seen her nibble the tassels while marking papers.

'So your dad left,' Hilary said. 'Big deal. You know there are children being tortured in Somalia?'

'Go suck Fidel Castro's dick,' I said.

I don't know why I tell her anything.

I sometimes go stand by the pay phone outside the Whitley's Wine Garage and pick it up, read the emergency numbers and listen to the tone, like I'm about to call him. I keep a line of people behind me waiting as I hold the dead receiver to my ear and go through the charade of nodding and hanging up. He called me once since he left, sounding concerned about my grades, congratulating me on scoring a point in netball, asking with purpose when the holidays were coming up, but never setting a date.

I came home once to find the taps in the kitchen and upstairs bathroom running on full blast. 'We can't afford the water bill as it is!' I yelled down the stairs at my mother as I got on my knees to see if the bath tap's head had come loose. Next door, Amy was grizzling quietly, pressing her pink flannel teddy to her face. 'And now you leave the taps on? What're you thinking?'

When I got downstairs, my mother was curled up with a glass of cranberry juice. 'Don't shout at me,' she said. 'I'm your mother.'

'Don't leave the water on like that!'

'I forgot about it,' she said. Her long brown hair was greasy and her fringe was stuck to her forehead. 'It doesn't matter, anyway. Once The Great One comes back, all these earthly troubles won't mean a thing.'

'Oh, right,' I snapped. 'Oh right. I forgot.'

'Go get your mother something to eat.'

'Why don't you ask the Great One to make you a fuck-ing sandwich?'

'I don't like that language, Sara.'

'It's an *earthly* trouble, don't worry about it!'

She only perks up when the church group is due. She bathes Amy in the morning, does some laundry and puts on one of her chiffon tunics. She wears the Italian perfume that my dad got her and clears the magazines and empty pasta cartons out of the living room. She looks quite nice with make-up on and dangly pearl earrings, she reminds me of the old days when she looks like that, but instead of being able to talk to her more easily I feel more removed. She has this drunk look in her eyes, spacious and immense, she looks over and through me, as if full of incandescent power.

The Disciples of Light greet me when they see me in the kitchen. The one that talks most often is a middle-aged lady, with skin like crumbling paste. Their leader is a man with dark glasses.

'I haven't seen you around, Sara,' the lady says when she sees me. 'How's school?'

'Don't know,' I mutter, wanting to cuss her out but not having the courage with the other members looming around. I fiddle with the lid on a bottle of flavoured water and refuse to meet her eye.

'We know this is a difficult time,' she says. 'But The Great One tests us all. In the last days, the tests will become harder.'

'Do you have any skimmed milk?' asks another member. She's an old Indian lady in a large green sweater, and she's peering into our fridge. 'I'm lactose intolerant, you see.'

'We only have the one with the green label,' I say.

'Ah, that's inconvenient.'

My mother appeared from the living room, smiling like

a hostess. 'I'll have Sara run down to McManaman's. It closes at seven, doesn't it, sweetie?'

'I don't know,' I said.

As my mother dug in her purse, the leader spoke up and said that some snacks – he specified caramel wafers – wouldn't go amiss. My mother gave me seven dollars and a quarter and the leader stopped me again at the door. 'Do you have enough for a box of Percocets? I have a headache coming on.'

'Eat my *shit!*' I spat out. Mom looked shocked, but said nothing.

That night, as I loitered around the light of the all-night Dollarama, I called dad on the pay phone and he promised to meet me after school. I forged a note that the blonde woman at Reception didn't even read and skipped half the day. I smoked a cigarette before walking to the bus stop through the field, crushing the butt into the mud. It had rained hard that morning and my sneakers were a mess by the time I reached Mikey's Pancake House.

Dad was a couple of minutes late. My stomach lurched when I saw him in a blue shirt, recognising and processing his grey hair and tanned skin, taking a moment just to get used to the sight of him.

'Sara!' He hugged me and I swallowed hard, feeling like an idiot because I wanted to throw up. 'It's great to see you.'

'Hi, dad.'

'Should we get a table?' He strode into the restaurant with purpose, joking with the waitress about the weather and telling me to get whatever I wanted.

'Your shoes are a mess,' he said.

'I know,' I said.

'How's Amy?'

'Fine.'

'And mom?'

'She's... fine.'

'Good! Good, I was worried about you guys.'

I let him talk about work. He recently went to Budapest and met one of his old college friends who played international ice hockey. I kept telling myself that I would fill the next silence with my declaration, my plea. I would tell him everything that had happened in such a way that he would hug me like when I was little and promise that it was out of my hands now.

My chocolate chip pancake came and I drowned it in chocolate and vanilla syrup.

'You and your sweet tooth!' Dad laughed. He ate with enthusiasm and asked me about school.

'You know,' I said. 'My friend Freda? She's on the netball team now. I was thinking of joining.'

'You should! Great exercise.'

Every time I opened my mouth, I smothered my own words with my food. My mouth felt gritty, like I was eating sugared sand, but I continued. I cleared my plate and dad downed his coffee.

'You know, Sara,' he said. 'It's kind of complicated, but I can't come home right now.'

I cycled the grit around my tongue like I was mixing cement. 'Okay.'

'I've met someone. Well, you're old enough now for me to tell you about her. You'd really like her, she owns horses. You know when we went horseback riding? Well, she'd love to meet you. But things are so crazy at the moment with everything. Maybe you could come for dinner at Christmas, hmm?'

'You need to come back now," I said, not knowing if I had said the words out loud or thought them.

Dad's smile vanished. 'Now don't be difficult, Sara. That's the noise I don't need right now.'

I said nothing. The leftover syrup on my plate reminded

me of mud. I was definitely going to puke.

'I've bought you dinner, haven't I?'

It was silent until the cheque came and my dad brightened again to charm the pretty waitress. When we left the restaurant, he patted my shoulder. 'I'll call you, Sara, okay?'

'Okay,' I said, and he hesitated.

'Do you, um, need a ride? Although my car's a bit of a mess...'

'No, I'm good.'

He straightened and nodded. 'Okay! Well, see you, baby girl!' He waved at me before he turned the corner and I waved back.

It was three-thirty already and the sky had brightened to a pale yellow. I walked down Main Front and Twenty-Fourth to Henrikson Boulevard and got my usual 457 bus.

We seemed to lose the ground through the tunnel. I sat back in my seat and breathed deeply through my mouth as a purple light shot through the aisle and dashed across my face. I decided to spend the leftover seven twenty-five in my pocket, not on my cigarette fund but custard doughnuts from the bakery on Eighth. I thought Amy and I could eat them together and watch *Wizard of Oz*, like we had last Thanksgiving.

The bus slowed at Hansen and I put my hand on the rail to steady myself.

The old man in the priority seat shook his head at me like he understood everything. 'It's gonna be a *good* day!' He assured me. 'It sure is! A *good* day *to*-day!'

'I guess so,' I said, and exited the bus.

The noon sky looked purple and the sun still shone.

MY FATHER'S SON

Victoria Stevens

When Peter Harrison hangs himself with his bed sheet in his cell at Highpoint Prison, it makes the six o'clock news. *South's Most Prolific Serial Killer Found Dead*. Cal and his mum watch it over microwave meals, between her shifts at the hospital. She gets up and switches the channel over before he can hear the rest of the bulletin.

It's all anyone talks about at Lakeview High School the next morning, students huddling in the corridors like it's some sort of sordid secret and not just fact.

'Did you hear about that murderer?'

'I heard he plaited his sheets together and tied them to the light fixture.'

'*I* heard when they found him his legs had gone all black.'

'I can't believe Mrs Wallis actually *taught* him!'

Cal never understands why people get so excited about Harrison – it wasn't like he'd been an Olympic gold medalist or a film star or a Premiership football player. He was a *killer*. He'd murdered a bunch of teenagers, most who'd even gone to the same school they were stood in now. The thought doesn't excite Cal, it makes him feel sick.

By lunch time the topic, thankfully, has worn thin. People return to their usual gossip, which Cal doesn't mind because Cal is invisible and it's hard to talk shit about someone if you can't even remember their name.

He heads to the canteen, to buy a value meal-deal with the change his Mum left on the counter before she went to work this morning. Carrot and coriander soup, or a tuna sandwich. He chooses the soup and wonders as he pays whether William has been let out of Maths yet. William is his best friend – no, his *only* friend. He's still thinking about it as he starts towards the tables, which is why he doesn't see the forwards of the rugby team approaching.

He does notice them when Alex Cramer pushes past him with such force that he loses his grip on his tray and his lunch tips down his front and onto the canteen floor. Someone laughs. Everyone laughs. Cramer turns around. Cal can see his pulse jumping in his neck, thick from the anabolics swimming in his blood. 'Fucking watch where you're going!' Cramer spits, shoving him again. 'Little shit!'

Cal can feel the soup burning the skin of his stomach where it's seeping through his shirt, but he ignores the stinging. He keeps his eyes down until the laughter fades away and he's sure Cramer and his friends are gone.

Empty-handed, he finds William in their usual place, sitting at the table tucked right into the corner. His friend waves over at him, smiling goofily, always cheerful. Sometimes Cal tries to remember how the two of them became friends, but he always comes up blank. Perhaps it wasn't because of a specific thing, no defining moment. Theirs is an odd friendship, he knows that much.

'You look like you've been shot,' William says as Cal slides into the seat opposite him.

'What?"

'Your shirt. You look like you've been shot.' Cal looks down at his chest. The soup has left a damp stain right in the middle, complete with little trails where the rivulets dripped down his torso. 'Blood isn't orange.'

'Well *yeah*, but...' William trails off, shaking his head. He smiles instead, taking his bacon panini out of its packet and breaking it into halves, pushing one across the table to Cal. 'Anyway. You see the news about Harrison?'

'Hmm.'

'Can't believe he's gone. What's Lakeview going to be famous for now? He was the one thing putting us on the map.'

He was all we had going for us.'

'He was a *serial killer*,' Cal says. 'Not exactly something to be proud of.'

'Yeah, but *still*.'

They eat their sandwich in silence. Cal doesn't mind silences with William, because William doesn't mind them with him. They have perfected the art of coexisting.

'This is gross,' William says, pulling an anemic-looking piece of bacon from the bread. 'God. I bet Harrison got better food up at Highpoint.'

'Probably.'

William throws the sandwich down with a sigh. 'Fucking government. You kind of remind me of him, you know.'

'Who?'

'Harrison,' William says. 'You done the English homework?'

'No,' Cal says. He never does the English homework. William rolls his eyes and picks up the sandwich again. Cal watches him as he picks at the edges. 'Why do I remind you of Harrison?'

'What?'

'Harrison. You said I remind you of Harrison.'

William pulls a face, leans over the table to ruffle his hair. 'Yeah, you both need a haircut.'

'So I don't look like him?'

William shrugs one shoulder. 'Not really. You wanna copy mine?'

Cal shakes his head.

As soon as he gets home, Cal Googles Harrison. He's got dark hair and a cleft chin, and his nose is too big for his face. He and Cal could be siblings, if he wasn't in his forties. He's far too old to be Cal's brother. Not too old to be his dad, though.

Cal had stopped asking Mum who his father was around his sixth birthday, when she'd shut his questioning down so hard that he'd cried into his caterpillar cake. The topic may have been blacklisted for a decade, but that doesn't mean Cal hasn't thought about it. Cal thinks about it all the time.

Cal looks into Harrison further. He killed seven people in total, two boys and five girls, all teenagers. Chopped their heads clean from their necks. In his mugshot, taken the same year Cal was born, he looks like a man who regrets nothing. Harrison grew up just a few streets from where Cal lives, and graduated from Lakeview High School in 1979. The same year as Cal's mother. They'd probably been in the same class. He tells William the news in English, face flushed with excitement. 'Harrison was arrested the month after I was born,' he says. 'He was in Mum's year.'

William raises an eyebrow. 'So?'

'So he could, logistically, be my Dad.'

'Your *Dad*? What the fuck are you talking about?'

'You... said I reminded you of him?'

'Yeah, because you're both *weird* looking,' William says. 'Jesus, Cal. I wasn't actually suggesting you were related.'

'But you said...'

'It was a joke!' William laughs. 'I was joking.'

'But it *fits*,' Cal says furiously. 'That's why she won't talk about him, William. Because he's a *murderer*.'

'Peter Harrison is not your *dad*. Don't start making up conspiracy theories about it, the freak's dead and buried.'
Cal frowns but says nothing. The idea is too fully formed to let go so suddenly.

The thing about not having a father is there's always half of you missing. The thing is, he's nothing like his mother – so maybe he is everything like his father.

His father's first victim was a young woman. Her name was Eleanor and she was in the Lower Sixth at the same time as him. When the police questioned his motive for that first kill, Harrison came up blank. *She was too pretty*, he shrugged. *It annoyed me.*

Cal spends the next couple of days wondering if there's an Eleanor in his own class. There are lots of good-looking girls, and even more who have made an art out of pretending that he doesn't exist. He settles on a girl called Hannah. Blonde, five foot four, cute. He follows her home from school, waits until the road is deserted and then hits her with his old cricket bat. He takes her limp body to the shed at the bottom of the garden and ties her down on the table.

His father decapitated his first victim. Cal finds the biggest knife from the kitchen, the one with the longest blade. The first strike reveals the bone of her spinal column: off white. Blood pools in her clavicle. The pain brings her to and she wakes sharply, mouth wide as she tries to scream. Nothing comes out. Cal raises the knife again and brings it down in the same place as hard as he can. This time it goes through the bone, right down to the wood of the table. The head separates, falls to the floor with a wet thud, her eyes twitching.

Cal stands and watches as the blood soaks into the carpet. It's everywhere; on the floor, on his clothes, covering his hands, dripping over the table edges. He sucks some off his thumb. It's warm, thick. He swallows it down.

There is no doubt; he is definitely his father's son.

Cal sleeps fourteen hours straight and wakes up refreshed.

'Someone's in a good mood,' William says when he walks into the classroom.

'He was an amateur,' Cal slides into the seat beside him. 'Decapitation is too messy.'

William gives him a look. 'What?'

'Harrison. He was an amateur.'

'I'm pretty sure *professional* homicidal maniac isn't a real job title, Cal.'

'I'm being serious.'

William tenses and untenses his jaw. 'Why are you still thinking about this guy? I told you to let it go.'

'It's *clumsy*,' Cal presses. 'There's got to be better ways of doing it. More efficient ways.'

He turns his attention to the whiteboard at the front of class. William stares at the side of his head for a long, long time.

Cal can't stop thinking about it. The weight of the knife in his hands, the fear in her eyes. He thinks of his dad and wonders if he felt the same after his first kill. Cal doubts he felt this good, because he waited almost four months before his next time. He isn't sure of Number Two's name, but she's in the year above him. He tries to knock her out the same way, cricket bat to the back of her head, but he hits too hard and instead of knocking her out it cracks her skull. She doesn't make a noise, just sways slightly before falling face-first onto the pavement. There's another cracking noise as she makes contact. Probably her nose.

Cal kicks at her waist. She doesn't move. He bends to check her pulse, two fingers pressed to her neck, but he feels nothing.

'Fuck!' he shouts, kicking her harder. He'd had so much planned for this one, and he didn't even get to take her to the shed.

Cal is back in the shed with Number Three, back where he belongs. Back where he can't fuck up. He has moved all his favourite knives from the kitchen to a display on the wall, hung up neatly by size. He's taped bin bags to the windows and there are plastic sheets on the floor this time round to make cleaning up easier; he won't make the same mistakes twice.

'You don't have to do this,' she tells him.

He tightens the cable ties binding her wrists and ignores her. She's too busy struggling against her restraints to notice him choosing a knife from the display until he's standing with the blade pressed flat against her neck. '*Please!*' she begs again. There's snot dangling from her left nostril, and the shed smells like urine from where she pissed herself earlier. Cal is suddenly and violently repulsed by her. 'I won't tell anyone, I swear! If you let me go, I'll... I'll...'

'What?' he snaps, speaking for the first time. 'Stop making my life a living hell?' She recoils, her eyes tracking his face desperately for something, anything she might recognise. 'Who are you?' she says, but it doesn't matter, not anymore. She stops asking questions around the same time he cuts off her first toe.

Cal chooses Number Four very carefully. Alex Cramer, the boy who made him spill his soup. Cal takes his mother's car while she sleeps between shifts and follows Alex Cramer home from football practice. He drives slowly, waits until he is walking down an empty street. He hits him from behind. His legs buckle and he flies forward, crumpling in on himself like paper. Cal drives forward over the body and then reverses back, forward and reverse, the bones crunching underneath his wheels like the gravel on his driveway. It's nothing like the first, but it's better than the second. Someone should have done him a long, long time ago.

Cal hasn't seen his mother in over a fortnight. She's always doing double shifts lately, and she leaves notes sometimes, but Cal doesn't read them. Why does he need a mum when he's got a dad? He does Number Five in the shed again. She is still unconscious as he carries her down the garden, her breathing shallow and her body limp from the secobarbital. He strips her naked and ties her down, making sure that she can't move. She doesn't stir. Cal dims the lights and double checks the locks before returning to the table. He stands and stares, taking her all in. She is so beautiful it almost seems a shame to destroy her. He leans over for a closer look, traces the faint blue lines of her veins with the tip of his blade, follows it from the pale flesh of her thigh up across the jut of her hipbones, settling in the valley between her breasts. He angles the blade, hovers it just above the skin stretched taut across her neck, and then plunges the knife straight into her sternum.

The rush hits him immediately, surges through him, leaves him reeling. He lets out a breathless laugh, dizzy from the sight of the blood as it spills around the blade, warm as it wets his fingers. He switches hands, drags the knife downwards towards her navel. The wound is uneven, jagged. Blood blooms in the dip of her belly button, unfurling like a carnation. Cal can taste it in the air, right on the tip of his tongue. She tastes like parma violets and the Chanel perfume she steals from her mother's vanity dresser. By the time he finishes his hands are covered in blood, sticky and itchy where it's beginning to dry along his forearms.

Number Five dies slowly. She doesn't scream once.

Cal catches William staring at him in class. More than once. It makes Cal's skin feel too tight for his body, like William knows his secret.

'What?' he eventually snaps at him in Chemistry. 'What do you want?'

'Nothing,' William says, his cheeks red. 'I just... you seem...'

'I seem *what*?'

'Different,' William says. 'Not yourself.'

Cal only smiles.

Cal is tired of using a knife. He doesn't know how his father killed all his victims the same way, how he didn't get bored. He wants to experiment. He takes Number Six *behind* the shed instead, binds her arms and legs and gags her mouth. He tips the fuel for the lawnmower over her body in a zigzag pattern, and then covers her with kindling and logs from the fireplace. He uses matches to set her alight and watches the flames burn from his bedroom window. Number Six is a human bonfire. Cal is still laughing when his mother comes home.

He takes his time planning Number Seven. It needs to be special, the final kill. The most memorable. It eats into his time; it's been weeks since he turned up for school, weeks since he had a conversation with someone that wasn't his mother. He's too focused. He even rejects William's calls. William keeps ringing. Cal isn't surprised when he turns up on his doorstep.

'Hey,' Cal says when he opens the door.

'Hey. Brought your homework for you.' He studies Cal's face. 'Everything okay? You sick or something?'

'No.'

'Can I come in, then?' Cal steps out of the way to let him into the hallway. They sit at the kitchen table. He makes them tea, finds a packet of biscuits to share. He realises he's missed company other than his own.

'What have you been up to, then?' William says eventually. 'Haven't seen you in ages.'

'Been busy.'

'Busy doing what?'

'Stuff,' Cal says.

William gives him a look, but Cal ignores it, focuses on the hard skin around his thumb nail. He can feel William watching him and it's distracting. He sighs, shakes his head. 'You wouldn't get it.'

'Try me.'

Cal sets down his cup, gathers his thoughts. 'Have you ever wished you could kill someone?'

'Get rid of them, you mean?' William says. 'Or, like, *actually* kill them?'

'Actually kill them. Cut their head off. Stab them in

their heart.'

'Can't say I have, no.' William pauses, glances sideways at him. '...have you?'

Cal is tired of keeping his secret. He wants to share it with someone, wants to brag and boast, and there's no one he trusts more than William.

'I've done way more than think about it,' he says.

Cal tells him everything. About Hannah and Cramer, about the other nameless four. About his shed, about his knives. About the pit at the end of his garden where he hacks their corpses into small pieces, seals them in freezer bags and buries them deep in the mud. Cal tells him everything and William says nothing. Just stares.

'Say something.'

'I'm just... it's a bit hard to get my head around,' William says.

'Do you want to see?' Cal says. 'I'll show you.'

He takes William down to the bottom of the garden. The door is unlocked. Cal is sure he locked it after Number Five, but he follows William inside anyway. It's dark. Maybe one of the bulbs blew out.

'This is it?' William says. 'This is where you killed them?' Cal doesn't answer. He stands in the middle of the shed and turns in slow circles. Where are all his things? His plastic sheets, his knife display? His toolbox, the rope, the cable ties? Why is everything covered in dust?

'Cal,' William says finally, voice level. 'What *is* this? What's going on with you?'

Cal can't look at him, can't look at anything except the section of the carpet where Number One's bloodstain should be. It should be right there, right beneath William's feet.

'Nothing,' he says.

'You know you can trust me, right? You can tell me anything.'

Cal says nothing. William takes a careful step closer,

rests his hand lightly on his shoulder. 'Is it about Harrison?'

'No.'

'Cal...'

'So what if it is?' He shrugs off William's hand. 'Maybe it's about him, or maybe it's about me. Maybe *I* need this. William, you need to let me have this.'

'Let you have *what*? What is it that you think you have? What do you get out of sitting here in the dark and fantasising about being like a man so fucked up they had to keep him in isolation for sixteen years?'

Cal stares at him. 'It's not *fantasy*.'

'Isn't it? If you actually murdered Alex Cramer then how the hell did he win the game for us last night?'

Cal becomes very still. He can feel his hands and throat, still.

'What?'

'He's not dead. You didn't kill him. You didn't kill *anyone*.'

The silence stretches out between them, but this time it's not comfortable, this time Cal minds it very much.

'Look, I know you think you need this,' William continues carefully. 'I know you think this is what you want, a father. But *Peter Harrison*? Why him? He's not even alive anymore!'

'Why are you trying to ruin this for me?'

'I'm not, I'm... I'm trying to *help* you!'

Cal shakes his head, backs away. He is so close to finishing, so close to finding his last victim. Seven, just like his father. He is just like his father, he has to be. What else does he have? This is what he's wanted his whole life, somewhere to belong. He can't expect William to understand why it's so important to him; William's never had a family that was anything other than whole.

'I trusted you. I told you everything.'

'He's not your Dad,' William says. 'I'm sorry, but he's not

your father. He's just some psychopathic nobody who –'

'Don't,' Cal says, voice cold, flat.

'Cal you need to –'

'Shut up! Just shut up!' He screws his eyes shut and clamps his hands over his ears to block out William's voice. He focuses his thoughts on Harrison instead. Harrison beaming as he brings out Cal's caterpillar cake at his sixth birthday party, Harrison pushing him on the big kid swing at the park for the first time. Harrison teaching him to tie his shoes, to ride a bike. He pictures him and Harrison and his mum, all sat together. A real family.

When Cal opens his eyes the shed is silent and he has his hands around William's neck. His friend has stopped talking. There are long streaks of red along Cal's forearms, scratches he didn't even feel. William's hair has fallen in his face. Cal has a sudden urge to brush it out of his eyes, to be gentle the same way William has always been gentle with him. Gentle and patient and consistent. Why does his father need this from him? Why does he have to hurt William too? Can he not still have Harrison as a dad without being any-thing like him? Perhaps this legacy isn't his to continue, per-haps this isn't even what his father would want. More images flash through his mind; Harrison teaching him to drive, Harrison watching him graduate high school. Harri-son sat at the front of the church at his wedding, loving him even though he's different.

Cal releases his hands. William folds in on himself once, twice, and falls to the floor. The hair is gone from his eyes. Cal can see his face now, pointing up at the shed ceiling, but it looks wrong, off-colour. His lips are purple at the edges; he looks cold. Cal takes one of the blankets from the dusty pile in the corner and tucks it around him, smooths it over his legs and under his arms to keep him warm. He lowers himself to the carpet, lies down beside him. William doesn't stir. There's a hole in the ceiling, directly above them, and

Cal can see the sky through it, grey with clouds. He hopes it doesn't rain on them.

'Don't worry,' Cal tells William cheerfully. 'I'll get my dad to patch it up.'

NOT THE ONE

Maria Highland

The first time I met Jake, I thought he was an arsehole; we were drinking in a park and he started throwing chunks of bread at me. When he left, I stuck my middle finger up at him. We met again at a house party. He pushed me onto a plate of pizza, and I slapped him across the face. We sat on the sofa laughing about nothing. His knee jerked up and knocked a bottle from my hand into my mouth. We stayed there laughing: him keeled over, me with a chipped tooth. Everyone knew we liked each other but we spent the summer in denial. I knew he wasn't over his previous relationship, but his next girlfriend didn't. They bonded over *Call of Duty* on PlayStation. She ripped the sticker off his flat peak cap, not knowing it was worthless without it. He screamed until his face turned red, but still asked her to be his girlfriend. He broke her heart; mine remained intact. Now she's my best friend. We laugh about him as we run riot on *Call of Duty* and I warn her about arseholes.

Lewis was a weird one. We met on a hot summer day. We'd all gone to a field for drinks and a picnic. By evening, the vodka got the better of him: he tried to steal my rings, bit my finger and manhandled me. Then to compensate, he gave me a yellow dandelion for my hair. On the way home he tried to hold my hand and kept asking me why I didn't like him. I laughed and told him we were friends. We never spoke about that night again. I gave him advice about girls and he made fun of me. On Halloween I dressed as a zombie and he was a ninja. We stole a bottle of champagne and drank it, giggling like children. He said he liked a girl, and I asked him who and how could I help. It became a guessing game; I was naming all the girls in our group. After a while, I gave up. He looked sheepish and I said it was time to go back downstairs. Four months later he met his sweet, curly haired, hazel eyed girlfriend, cheated on her, and she forgave him. She's one of my best friends.

Luke was intense; the first boy to tell me he loved me. I panicked and ran. He said he fell in love with me the night we all went for a walk through the woods, past a farm and into a park. In the pitch black at 3am, we linked pinkies, using our phones as flashlights. We all sat on the tennis court and watched the stars, talking nonsense about life and our futures. He said he'd never met someone like me. I laughed and said we were only young and didn't know anything about love. He said I interested him; he wanted to read me like a book. I broke his heart. He said I destroyed him and he couldn't be around me. When I saw him six months later, he had a girlfriend. She was everything I wasn't: blonde, tall and in love with him.

Gordon told me he liked my lips and that he didn't normally go for thin girls. He was a known player but a nice boy. We played *Fifa* and he picked China vs Albania as the teams, joking about my small eyes. He said that Albanians and Russians hate each other on *Grand Theft Auto*. I met his mum and turned red when she said something to him in Albanian. He laughed at me; she'd said I was pretty, but he told me not to get a big head. He hinted at me being his girlfriend and threw 20p down my top. I threw the coin back at him. We were watching a film when he said he loved me. I pretended to be asleep. By September he had a girlfriend.

I didn't stick around to meet her.

Me and Harry had always been friends and started speaking more in winter. We'd always got along and joked about stupid things. He suggested we watch a movie; I jokingly said yeah, *Barbie* or *The Bratz*. Eventually, I gave in and we went to see *Scream 4*. He jumped at a scene and I called him a pussy boy. We thought the film was terrible, so watched another one at his house. He put his arm around me and I didn't shrug it off. He hugged me goodbye. By Spring, I was his girlfriend. He told me he loved me after three months. I didn't believe him, but said I did anyway. Harry had said he couldn't see us breaking up; I told him he'd get sick of me. After 15 months, it was over. He rage-quit the relationship then asked for another chance. I apologised. Three months later, he was out with a taller, thinner version of me. Harry told me that we'd get along, and that her father was a cheating arsehole like mine.

I found Jack in a corridor. I'd been to a house party and he'd been out. I was drunk and he was high. I thought he was Spanish and he thought I had nice eyes. We sat in the kitchen having a midnight feast. He asked too many questions and laughed too loud, munching on falafel and hummus. We spoke about nothing; cars, jobs, religion, spirits, afterlife and food till 6am. We saw each other again. Midwinter, we sat on a long striped sofa with tasselled cushions outside a shisha bar in Queensway. He called it Arab Central. We drank mint tea, puffed watermelon shisha and quoted *Pineapple Express* and *Little Nicky*. In the car he asked if he could kiss me and I said maybe another time. Seven months later, I was his girlfriend. Two months after that, I was his ex-girlfriend and a week later we said we missed each other. Six months later, we still say it. He said he loved me. I had said that well, maybe, I loved him, too. Maybe. The other day, his new girlfriend added me on Facebook.

ISABELLA

Idunn Elvrum

As far as the public is concerned, I'm a Starbucks barista. As far as *I'm* concerned, I'm a professional annoyance and proud of it. Analytical skill, immaculate timing, reading people – these are only some of the qualities you need if you want to do what I do.

People are easily annoyed, and a typical day of trying to do it well starts even before I get to work.

Number one: commuting. Endless potential. London buses have stopped accepting cash, so I make sure I put that extra effort into fumbling for my Oyster card, blocking other passengers. Before I leave my flat, I spray myself in so much Lynx you could mace a small grizzly bear with it. If there are many seats available on the bus, I make sure I sit next to another passenger, regardless. I don't acknowledge this person, as this would make me seem like a creep. See, analytical skill. I don't smile, I just sit down next to them like it's natural. It works best if there are only one or two people on the bus.

After that, I take the Tube. I wear headphones and crank the volume all the way up. I listen solely to songs contrived to stick in your head. People might think I'm weird for blasting Nicki Minaj at half seven in the morning, but they'll also have that *boom badoom boom boom badoom boom* bass stuck in their heads for a good couple of hours. I tap my feet vigorously. I slowly savour my breakfast from Tupperware boxes, pungent foods like tuna, curry or anything swimming in vinegar.

Then number two: work. If you think I'm a 26-year-old working at Starbucks out of choice, you are correct. There are few people more irritable than those waiting for caffeine in the Conduit Street morning rush. Make no mistake, I make excellent coffee drinks, but I'll be sure to fuck you around in the process.

'Sir, would you like to try our special blend Guatemalan expresso today?'

Make sure to emphasise the 'X' in espresso. This pisses coffee enthusiasts off.

'No thanks.'

'You sure? It's definitely one of the better eXpressos we've had in, medium roast, grown in volcanic soil –'

'*No thanks.*'

'It's only 40p extra –'

'No thanks, *bloody hell!*'

'Alright then, sir, what's your name?'

'David.'

The man on the street will hereby know you as 'Dawwid'. Congrats, you've been Starbucks-baptised.

Why do I do all of this? I used to get annoyed all the time. Now I don't. It's that simple. If something irks me even slightly, I consider it a case study and use it for myself if I can. I don't shout, I don't raise my voice, I don't lose my cool. I just don't get annoyed.

Well, I say 'don't', but I really mean 'didn't'.

We've got this Polish girl at work now. Isabella. I call her Isabella because she asked me to call her Iza. Iza picks up all the extra shifts, Iza always smiles at everyone even if they're dicks when they order, Iza happily makes those separate soy and skinny lattes in different pitchers even though they're for the same group of friends. Iza laughs when I write 'Izzy' or 'Iza' or 'Isabel' on her cup when she finishes her shift.

She giggled hysterically when I put 'Cark' for some guy that said his name was 'Mark with a C'. Then she apologised for me. She shrugs when I intentionally use the section of the espresso machine that she's pre-closed, and says she doesn't mind doing it again. *Everyone* minds closing down the espresso machine.

When I come home after a shift with Iza, my head hurts. I struggle to fall asleep. So I don't sleep much. You'd think that wouldn't be a problem working in a coffee shop. But there I am, bright and early for the morning shift and Iza pulses the blender while whistling cheery tunes, like it's some fucking jukebox. I doubt *injecting* the sodding Guatemalan espresso would help me. I've considered taking up smoking again. I probably would, if it wasn't for the fact that I make fuck-all and a penny an hour.

When my co-workers plan drinks in Soho after work, they try to do it discreetly, while refilling sugar sachets and stirring sticks or getting more gingerbread syrup from the back room. When I overhear them and invite myself, it's a blast. It used to be. Now, Iza *tells* me they're going out and that I should *come*. She always adds 'though' at the end of her sentences.

'You should come with us though, we're going to the Yard!' she beams, flashing her straight, white teeth behind burgundy lipstick.

'Thanks, *Isabella*, but I actually have plans tonight,' I say, restocking the fridge with semi-skimmed milk and gritting my teeth. I'm not dragging this description out for dramatic effect; I know perfectly well that she annoys me. More than shitty Wi-Fi connections and Jonathan from Spotify.

Her hair bobs up and down in long, dark red curls as she hurries between the espresso machine and the customers. I wonder how often she dyes it, that colour can't be natural. She annoys me because no matter what I do, I can't seem to annoy *her*.

I can't enjoy anything anymore. I notice more stuff that annoys me, now Iza's fucked me over. Not only about her, about everyone. I don't enjoy my routine anymore, it seems like a chore rather than the pleasure and comfort it's been.

I sit alone in my Wimbledon flat, watch Netflix, and think of Iza. I get chicken from the shop downstairs, and I think of Iza. I book the shifts she doesn't take, and I think of her. It's not normal to be in a jolly mood all the time, I don't buy it. *Everyone* gets annoyed. Even Isabella Brzozowska. I just haven't found what ticks her clock yet. On Tuesday, I found out that Tom has changed shifts because he's going out on a warehouse rave for his birthday. Twat. So I'm on closing duty with *her*, and I'm trying to think up an arsenal of nuisances. Just Iza and I, alone for hours.

When she's in the bathroom, I cut a tear in the espresso residue bag. There are hardly any customers in.

'What are you doing this weekend, Harry?' she asks when she comes back.

'Oh, you know,' I say. No one knows, I do sod-all but work and sit at home, watching shit telly and playing guitar. 'Work,' I finish.

'I have an extra ticket to see alt-J if you want to go, though,' she says.

I freeze. I actually quite like them.

'Just you and me?' I ask.

'Yes, if you want,' she says, running tap water over a sponge.

'Err... thanks, but I don't like that kind of music,' I say. If I wanted to go I'd buy my own ticket, there's no way I'd give her the satisfaction.

'Oh, really?' she says, sounding disappointed. 'It seems like the type of music you would like though.'

'Why?' I start biting my nails, some people find that annoying. Her big, blue eyes look at me. Through me.

'It's cool music, you're cool,' she says, with a little laugh.

I have nothing to say, so I start cleaning tables. Iza locks the front door and checks that no one is downstairs or in the loos. I hog the docking station and put my playlist on, *All About That Bass* by Meghan Trainor comes on, it's already stuck in my head. Small price to pay if it ticks Iza off, though. Of course, it bloody doesn't, she laughs and does a little jive as she puts the chairs up on the tables. I can feel my ears going warm.

Then *My Humps* by the Black Eyed Peas starts playing, and she spins around.

'Do you actually listen to these normally?'

'Well, yeah? They give me energy,' I say, nodding one time too many.

'Haha, you are so funny, though, Harry!' she says, and pats my shoulder as she passes me.

I'm left standing there like some idiot, and there's nothing I can think of that I haven't tried to annoy her. She cleans the espresso machine while humming *Dream a Little Dream of Me* over the music I'm playing. I don't understand her, so I frantically scrub the fridge trying to think of something. I definitely won't sleep tonight if I can't get this right.

Iza takes the big, black espresso bin bag out, and it rips all over the newly swept floor.

'Shit!' she says.

'Oh, *no!*' I echo, grinning.

'That was clumsy of me, I'm sorry, Harry. You can just leave if you want, I will clean this up.' She's still sporting the toothy smile that she never wipes off, whiter than the KKK, goddamn Colgate models are jealous.

'I thought you had plans tonight?' I say.

'Yes, but just for drinks. I'm Polish, I can drink any time.' She chuckles at her own joke.

That's fucking *it* for me.

'Why the *fuck* don't you ever get pissed off, you stupid *bint? What's wrong with you? Huh?* I can't bloody take this anymore, I'm quitting this fucking job, you're not fucking *normal!*' I slap a Guatemalan espresso bag and send it flying off the counter. I haven't shouted for a very long time, and think I lost the hang of it; I have no idea what I'm saying.

Iza stands there like some fierce fucking statue, but the smile is gone – and somehow, it makes me uneasy. Her cheeks are all rosy and her makeup is intact after seven hours at work. I breathe heavily and feel sweat drops forming on my forehead. My heart is pumping battery acid.

'Harry, I know exactly what you're doing,' she says.

'*What?*'

'I know you like to annoy people, so I wanted to see how you would react if you couldn't annoy me,' she says, gathering the espresso grinds on the floor together with her foot and looking me right in the eye.

'You *what?*' I say, moving closer.

'You heard me,' she says. 'But just so you know, I actually do hate this song.'

James Blunt's *You're Beautiful* is playing.

I stand there for a second. Then I grab her cheeks with both hands and kiss her, before I rethink it. And she kisses me back. I pull away and just stare at her for a moment, before I realise I want to hold her close, so I do.

She smells of ground coffee, burnt milk and some kind of faint, floral perfume. Somehow it takes me back twelve years to my kitchen table, to eating porridge while watching my mother reading the Sun behind a vase full of purple lupins. Drinking her last ever cup of coffee.

Something inside me breaks, and I sob into Iza's hair as I pull her even closer against my chest. She clenches my jumper and I'm fourteen-years-old again.

'It's okay,' she says, voice muffled, her warm breath damp against my ribcage. I wipe my face with my sleeve and let go of her.

'You really are... very annoying, Iza,' I say.

'Am I really?' she says, raising an eyebrow and touching my cheek. But I have no answer. I grin.

'Maybe a little,' I say, and kiss her forehead.

'Will you let me annoy you again sometime?'

'Yes,' I say, smiling, and as we scoop the coffee grounds off of the floor together, I feel this annoying calm come over me.

POETRY

A CAT

Lloyd Cole

I spend half my life
on a bus and the other half
waiting for a 72 to trundle up
Barnes Bridge's rusty knuckle
and deliver me to Hammersmith
with 17 minutes of rattling gratitude
I don't have to trudge across the Commondale
or tiptoe past Red Lion – onwards off the bus
onto the Circle Line for 34
raw static minutes I glare
at a *terrific* advert and smirk and
sob because I don't need half-price
hair tonic but I've read it
20 times a minute
more and I might die because it's
SO DAMN FUNNY
(sigh)
I've ripped all my hair out so
I boldly weave across Liv Street past
crane-necked commuters
adults on scooters
newspaper looters
and behind those that are
criminally   unforgivably   slow
I shave my way onto the train
for Clacton, sunshine state of Essex,
perched upon a Rorschach test
beside a boozy businessman who
passes out wakes up pukes up

his dinner pints and dentures
which he catches wipes replaces, I
flit right across the carriage
and withdraw out of the window
because London's slipped away
we slither quick through stations grey
until we reach Thorpe where I sigh,
so close, a burnt out fire station husk
is propped against Pink sky –
three Floyd songs later I arrive
"Clacton in Bloom!" a hanging casket
two tracks more I'm at the drive
of number six I free the key
with 1930 and intrude
into my parent's home and there
a cat, a comma on the carpet, that
is Heaven.

STEIN SERIES
Hannah Hodson

Straw

Gardener, who paints the naked growing. Look at struggle and string and sting.

A noun is Eve Adam and Eve and grief. Fine silk falling upwards, silk falling, silk falling, milk sailing. Molecules balancing, silk falling, it is milk sailing, silk falling. Broken straw is straw failing.

Roar, roar, straw. Oh in roar ah in hay. Vowels in a bucket slush rinse pour. 7.01 String struggle sting. Sting struggle string. 7.03 Struggle sting string never only.

Silverware warning straw walk away wa. Wa wa string and sting and struggle each sip. Struggle and sting and string each sip never a moment the same always more room lips grasp lips vacuum

milk sailing.

Synthetic Petal

A tortured vein is a plant and a victim and an old woman. Odour is dying and breathing and an old woman almost breathless. A phoney is a fake plant, not dead not alive always breathless. The petals scentless because they are phony. Death prods the victim and the plant and the woman breathing. Death is relentless death is itchy.

Tender throat is a plant and a victim and an old woman. A synthetic petal is more dead and more alive than this. Phoney faux free from photosynthesis.

To be thriving with no expiry date is to be a phoney plant is it not. A synthetic petal means rootless lonely plant does it not. Why vanity is pathetic. Pathetic is nearly nothing. Beautiful synthetic petal.

An Engine

An engine in the middle of an orange and an edge is an email.

Essential Portion

Essential is at the essence of easy is it not. Easy is it not to be an essay, to be an essay. Why to examine an essay is to easel a seizure. An easel is a table on the ceiling in essence it is easy or easing.

Cushion

Creamy, why creamy, why vanilla breezy vanilla is a beige scoop. A sailor is smothered in vanilla. Beige and creamy warm dust; dusty villa. To sleep in vapour is to die vaguely on a cushion sheering wool. It does mean to smear beige.

HOLIDAY
Ellie Kennedy

from canoe to car
Ontarian lake water
in our dripping socks

a child's summer day
pool water splash
washing the melted crayon

one skinny lizard
under the villa's door gap
in scorching evening

SINGULAR

Chlo Edwards

city lights
the bench and I
on the bridge

walking home
everyone else
walks to work

a hundred flies
on my ceiling
one praying mantis

sea foam footprints
a tree trunk
struck

I watch
the raindrops
fall in my coffee

cold bed sheets
the door
bangs and bangs

HOPSCOTCH

Agne Sadaunikaite

8.
concrete filled balloons

6.
crucified love kites

7.
empty Russian dolls

5.
masochistic books

3.
poisoned daddy scowls

4.
noose and no scraped knees

2.
psychedelic sweets

1.
bad kids never sleep

RAW, INDIGENOUS

Agne Sadaunikaite

Raw, indigenous and sacred – she burns
a wooden figure. Never touch a girl
with skin that doesn't shiver. She'll take
your lungs and start a war with cherry leaves
she'll set your fingertips alight. Gunfire
powder stains her cheek. Rosy houses fall.
Their cherry leaves curl like drowning paper –
Wednesday. She picks up a ladybird
and blows away a wish. *Fly to the edge,*
she whispers, *never face South.* A prayer,
ritual and a bittersweet riot –
déclencher une guerre, baby. She picks stars
and names each after the King of Skies.
On her knees she chants a midnight song.
Satin smoke cloaks tomorrow's night and pyramids
collapse into dust. Black. A widow howls,
her dirty feet melt beneath the icy
heath. Scar across her thigh and a bloody
tear runs down her tongue. A lily petal
sinking in a ruby river, smelling of death
and drinking life, she'll be your last inmate.

FESTing rd yearning
Audrey Jean

resurfacing re
surfacing/espinho resurface
england of tears to cut your
        hair short at the back of
        your head   – under
    to catch breeze

    Idea of bees – MONUMENT
                    TEMPLE of fabric   softener
ideal of Sun, softer (dust   photons   waves   doré
            BLACKFRIARS&others

            sure facing the
atlantic/bliss surfacing remedy
sure of blissful reassurance   of life/
                    goldenhairphotos, her?

him? ,   (((warm sand

                    resurfacing
burncream heavenly
        , sticky   ,   bedshared

                    no
                    big boys don't cry
                    big boys don't cry
                    ghost at the back
                    of your head)   resurfacing

no, lodged in throat,
>   no no no (rock in mouth shaking head
>   and the blue/deep blue/icy, bare, heart-
>   burn cream

left all in espinho i thought i was wrong of course, cause im

>   resurfacing/resurfacing
>   ghost memories at

>   the back of close cut head at
the burn of deep blue heart   at
)) no, no – ease the throat, ease it, easy, ease,   eat
>   (undercooked croissants
>   honey spread /still in mouth

bliss still in taste, MISS DEEP BLUE
– SMALL TOWN WITCH, miss her, miss him, MISS JEAN, MISS
no

>   throat closing
>   england   ice burning
>   him missing/her missing, sun   missing

of difficulties remembering – of dashes permuting – of
>   /memry brdg opning

(still have letters, i steal
i nose in neckcrook inhale, letters of bridge
>   until next/espinho

>   heal

CHURCH

Brad Cohen

Wall to mantle the choirs of statues blaze, but no virgin's glare could annul our sermon. Blow argent smoke from your mouth, a pink and porcelain censer. Grey curls bloom in amber light from the street lamp, ghost lilies in our urban Eden. A drop gives in and plays lead on the glass stained by our breath.

Newborn, my arms hang from your shoulders, ankles crossed with yours. Your chin prickles my forehead. We are a carnal crucifix. Blood-rust rings from my glass brand a triquetra on your stomach: still tense. Five disciples stroke my scalp, run through the sweat-knot scourge. My knees weep on the ivory-white sheet from my last pillow-less confession.

Silent in your possession, an echoing hymn of exhalation. Your communion is a spatter on the mattress, already soaked in. Cool constellations on my calf. Here in our sanctuary, there's a murmuring crusade, their huffing organs a dirge to grind against. A few muted thuds from upstairs. Our voyeur above enjoyed the show.

CREATIVE NONFICTION

MOODLE: MY PORTAL TO HELL
Rufus H.B. Williams

Login. Forgot your password? Yes. Enter your student ID, WTF is that? I've been reduced to a number and a memorable password. I try again. This time, my ID has not been recognised.

Why Moodle? What *is* a Moodle? I thought it was called a noodle. That's what I called it for two days. I was corrected by a barman, 'No, mate – it's *Moodle.*'

My name is Rufus. I've been a university student for eleven days. Problem is, I'm completely disconnected from it all: every university day is trapped in there, in the Moodle. I'm having trouble getting my noodle round it.

I am in Halls. I'm in a room, not a hall but I say, 'I'm in halls.' It sounds as though I should be walking across quads in a cloak. There's ten smashed up cans of Skol Super strewn across my room; it's the beer with the power to stop the muscles in my lips from working.

Day 12. My Moodle asks me to login again. There's a picture of a monkey on the screen, at a typewriter. Am I the monkey or is the monkey already logged in?

Day 13. I have successfully logged in. I have entered the main frame. My room stinks of wet towels. I have a shower that floods the bathroom. I've tried to stop this from happening but I've failed.

Day 15. I've finished an essay. I need to turn it in – not in the classical sense, I will not be handing it to my teacher – but instead I must go deep inside the sterile world of the Moodle, where sentences carry little hope: *Work submitted here cannot be seen or marked by your tutor.*

Day 21. The Student Welfare Officer asks, 'Are you struggling, Rufus? Do you need some support?' The lady asking me is huge, with a yellow T-shirt. There's a part of me that wants to climb up on her lap and have her read to me.

'I am finding the Moodle a bit complicated,' I say.

'What bit?'

I want to say, *all of it*, I want to say, *the entire thing, including the name.* Instead I say, 'The modules'. This is another new word, *modules*. It sounds like it could be a sort of pod, a NASA project: *They are living in a module, miles above the earth's atmosphere.*

Day 26. An email informs me that my submission has not been received. The view of the car park from my window looks like a scene from *This is England*. I've cooked some pasta; it's hard in my mouth, like Coco Rocks. I'm going to chuck it and get a drink. As I walk to the off-license, I hum a song: *I need a mum to last forever.* A song from the movie *Rug Rats in Paris*. I like that film.

DUCKS & HORSES

Jalice Corral

My father is a dreamer. He dreamed us around the world. One day we'd be moving to his parents' cabin in West Virginia to avoid our state's heavy homeowner's tax. The next day we'd be off to California, where his cousin Joe lived or packing our bags for Wyoming, to join his friend, Doug the buffalo herder. We followed Uncle Richard to Las Vegas because nobody could beat dad at seven-card stud poker. After that we jetted off to Eastern Europe to farm alpaca fur. From there, a train to Spain where he'd teach English and explore our ancestry. And New Zealand, maybe by boat this time, also for alpacas. When I was twelve, he picked me up late from school with two comments: first, he was sorry; second, did I own a scarf or headband that I could tie into a hijab? And if not, how many would I need to buy? He'd decided we were moving to Egypt.

My father never progressed beyond talk, so we lived in the same house almost my whole life.

Shortly after my parents were married, when they were living in a small house three blocks inside the Baltimore city line, my father promised my mother that he would move them somewhere nicer. He assured my mother, who grew up among wild coconut, mamey, chironja, and her father's mighty tropical flowers in Puerto Rico, that he would move her to a farm. A promise that she in turn made to me, on his behalf. I had just graduated from kindergarten and was distraught over leaving my best friend. I finally conceded, on the condition that she buy me a pet duck.

Time passed. Each time my mother drove me to school, we passed a farm with a goat hutch and a shallow-dug pond and we had the same conversation.

'Your dad always says we'll move to a farm.'

'I know. You promised me a duck. I'm holding you to that.'

As a pre-teen working at the Loch Raven Elementary School fair, my father had discovered he was allergic to horses. On the drive between our house and school, on the same road as the farm my mother remarked on, cutting through woods, then fields, then farms, then suburbs, we passed a ranch.

20 acres and a barn FOR SALE.

'Maybe we should buy it, start a ranch,' he said.

'What would you do with a ranch?' I asked.

'Put some horses on it.'

'You're allergic to horses.'

'What? No I'm not.'

We didn't buy the ranch. It was still for sale when I left home for college.

In 1997, my father bought an undeveloped piece of land in the Puerto Rican mountains. He plans to build a house there so he and my mother can retire twenty minutes from her childhood home. He hasn't set foot on 'the land', as he calls it, since 2012. I went to check up on the plot last June, and confirmed that the neighbors go through it with a machete and let their cows graze to keep the weeds down. I sent pictures of it to my father, in his big red recliner in the suburbs of Maryland.

THE ANEMOI
Jesse Bedayn

It was the first night of the trip. We set up our campsite with
all our new gadgets: gas stove, sporks, satellite phone,
freeze-dried porridge, and nylon tents. We didn't need wood
for a fire, or rock to strike a spark: we turned knobs, ate
chicken noodle soup, and rolled into bed.

But that night it rained. At three in the morning we
found ourselves scrambling to get our nifty waterproof covers over both tents. It was pitch black outside, and all we
could see were the beams from our LED headlamps, flashing
about the campsite.

The wind had picked up substantially, and the tent
cover was thrashing; Marcus and Ryan began searching the
campsite for granite shards to stack on the tent flaps, ham-
mering spikes into the ground to secure the tent corners.
Miles and I grabbed our equipment, threw it into the tents
for shelter, and secured our backpacks to nearby trees. We
had to yell to be heard over the wind, and even then, it was
hard to make out what everyone else was saying.

Then it hit. All four of us paused, standing under the
rain, clothes whipping in the northern wind, Marcus and
Ryan holding the flapping corners of the tents, Miles and I,
backpacks hoisted over our heads. We gazed up. It wasn't
frightening; it was too impressive to just be frightening. It
was awful magnificence. The blasts of thunder seemed to be
pressing onto my back and shoulders, making me bend double, clutching my knees. It was like a gong the size of London, beaten by an enormous bludgeon, directly above our
heads. Anything I tried to yell was picked up and ripped

away by the wind. It was as if the Anemoi, gods of wind and storm, had been released for one last, passionate battle. Zeus joined in, his lightning flaring out of the black clouds, leaving our vision spotty with florescent shapes: whipping the tops of the mountains, as if to drive back the tallest peaks.

Our mountain location thrust us so close to the turmoil that we became participant hoplites, quivering in the Greek mountains or Trojan plains. Every beat of the gong seemed to strip us further from place and time. Our names didn't matter. BOOM. Our heritage was forgotten. BOOM. The satellite phone and nylon tents were nothing. We were left animal, filled with mere extinguishable flame. We could have been above the cliffs of Thermopylae two thousand years ago, or in East Africa discovering fire two hundred thousand years before that, it wouldn't have made a difference. I slowly straightened my back, removing my hands from my knees. I wasn't shaking any more and the pressure on my shoulders and neck had lifted.

I turned my face toward the sky again and my heart beat with the thrum of thunder.

PATTERNS
Fathima Begum

My father taught me all 26 letters of the alphabet and the
first hundred numbers and how to brush my teeth properly.
I remember him with my three year-old brother on his hip,
hovering over the cooker, making our lunch when my
mother was in hospital giving birth to my sister. He gave me
a beautiful gold necklace: two hearts, one above the other.

I don't remember any specific days. I was three years
and four months old.

A week before my sixth birthday, I stayed behind with
my Nana, Auntie and siblings while my parents travelled to
Saudi Arabia, to perform the pilgrimage to Mecca. When
they returned, I noticed a difference. My father was slim-
mer; the bulging stomach I'd struggled to wrap my small
arms around, had gone. The food usually served in our
household was replaced with simpler, healthier meals. I'd
been brought up on rich curries: chicken and aloo, lamb and
tomato, fish and pumpkin, okra baazi. Now, it seemed, for
the first time in twenty-five years, my father was embracing
English cuisine. The fragrant smells of masala, turmeric,
cumin, ginger and curry powder were replaced with roasted
meat, parsnips and carrots. I'd watch him from the kitchen
table, cooking a whole chicken, all crispy, brown and tender.
He'd carve it for dinner, sharing it out between the family.

He cooked like this for nearly five months. And then he
got worse.

The visits to the doctor's that started out slow became
frequent. Appointments turned into trips to the hospital.
Then one day, he didn't come back. The nurses said he had

to stay. They said that he would get better staying there. So we visited him. He was hooked on wires, beeping rhythmically as they carried oxygen into his body. He looked weak, tired. He wouldn't stop fussing, telling my mother which bills needed to be paid and where to go to pick up his daily newspaper. I didn't understand why he couldn't come home.

Weeks passed. My cousin Rumena took care of me. We sat in the dining room, me playing with her hair. I was doing my best to plait it. I heard my mother and aunt return, the sound of the front door shutting a little louder than it usually did. It had been a long day and I hadn't seen my mother at all. She started to cry. I got out of Rumena's lap.

I had never seen my mother cry. She was standing in the hallway, holding onto my aunt for strength. Rumena had followed me; I held onto her, gasping back tears. She tried to calm me with a packet of Opal Fruits. For the first time, I refused them. I was too frightened to swallow.

A few days later, my father's body came home for the last time, wrapped in a white cotton sheet, tucked into a shiny, russet coffin, carried by pallbearers into our living room. His friends surrounded him, leaving behind their prayers and tears. My mother stayed in bed; her friends tried to comfort her. She had decided to bury him in Bangladesh, the place of his birth: what he would have wanted.

The day after my father's funeral, my mother began wearing white. I'd never seen her looking so bland. Her favourite colours were turquoise, mustard yellow or burgundy maroon. Her saris were patterned with flowers, embroidered in lace or beaded in sequins. 'Nah! The sari is too plain,' I'd often hear her say, browsing the catalogues on our coffee table. These new white saris were missing all the things she loved. For four months and ten days she put flowers and lace aside and didn't leave her dead husband's home without reason.

The stories his friends told us about him felt distant.

'You should be proud to call him your father,' the elders said, chatting over the biryani mum always cooked for social gatherings at our house. But I didn't feel like the daughter of the main character.

I began to grow up without my father.

When I was sixteen, my sister Tahsin and I visited friends in Bradford. We went by coach. Annoyingly, Tahsin fell asleep beside me within the first hour. I had nothing to occupy me apart from the book I had picked up, *A Golden Age* by Tahmima Anam. It seemed an interesting read, but my mind kept drifting away.

I noticed the man sitting in front of me, repeatedly glancing me up and down. He had come onto the coach in Blackburn. I was a little uneasy. I put away my book and took out the Tupperware my mother had given me. Finally, the man turned around.

'You're from Liverpool, aren't you?' he said. He was wearing a white traditional salwar, and he recited my home address from memory. I felt a little better: I guessed he was an imam from a local mosque. 'I knew your father,' he said. 'We spoke of many things... He was a man of *many* things.' I nodded my head to be polite, to show I understood what he was talking about, but I didn't, not really.

'We went to Hajj together in 1999. Your parents, myself and my wife. We got separated after we arrived in Makkah. It was on the last day when I finished praying in the Masjid Al-Haram that I noticed your father sitting in front of me. I waited for him to finish praying and then we both rejoiced at seeing each other again.'

I wondered where the story was going.

'He would have loved to have seen his children grow up. We would have daily calls about you. I'd give news of my two boys and he did the same with you. You're not much older than my eldest.'

'You did? What else did he do?' I blurted, surprising my-self, '...Uncle?' I added, carefully. There was something about the way he spoke of my father, some authority others seemed to lack. I had stopped listening to the stories years ago, and most people had stopped telling them. But suddenly, on this bus, I missed my father.

The imam looked at me curiously.

'We grew up together in the same village in Bangladesh. He used to get me into trouble with our parents – well, that's not fair to say. There were a few occasions when I'd re-turn the favour,' he smiled, his eyes twinkling at the memo-ries. 'We would always get caught whenever we stayed out late. Our favourite game was the *dung guli*. It's a game some-where between golf and softball. You make shallow dents in the ground and place a piece of wood the size of an egg, in it. You take a long wooden stick to hit it from one dent to another.' He looked down at the Tupperware I had opened, with its mixture of fish shami kababs, chicken pakoras and keema puris.

'Would you like one?' I offered.

He chose a chicken pakora. 'These were your father's favourite. He used to love them for his evening snack with his tea.'

'What else did he like?'

'Studying. All the time,' he quipped. 'He was a hard worker, and determined. Did he tell you about the children's home?'

I remembered something vaguely, but shook my head.

'This was in the early nineties. There were children without parents and the imam at the mosque was having continuous meetings with the council. The only way, they said, to build a home, was to raise the funds ourselves. So me, your father and a couple of others did our best to put forward as much as we could, then asked the community to help. At one point, we didn't think we could do it. But your father wouldn't give up. He held community meetings and printed off leaflets about it, posting them through letterboxes. I think it mattered to him more than anyone else.' His voice was soft.

'He did all that?' I asked, feeling proud, unexpectedly.

'No one cared. They kept themselves to themselves until your father made it his mission.'

'I heard about the home once. I didn't know he had such a huge part of it.'

'You should visit. They made a plaque for him with his name engraved. They have it on a special bench in the gardens.'

It is sixteen years since my father's passing. I sit on a neat wooden bench and watch children playing contentedly among the trees. The plaque is on the bench, at my back, under my shoulder blades. The sun is raining sparkles on my face and hands, but I already feel warm. A child runs up, no more than three. I kneel down at her level. She pulls my face with her little hands and kisses me on my forehead, then runs away, laughing.

TALES FROM THE TRIM TABLE
Hannah Vally

I was only fourteen when I 'trimmed' weed for the first time. It was winter break in my freshman year of high school, and I was visiting my dad in Mendocino County. After my sister and I flew into Sacramento and drove the three hours north to his house on the ridge of a mountain deep in the woods, my father sat us down in the dining room and told us that he needed three pounds trimmed by the morning.

He took us through it step by step, gave us our 'fiskars' (the insider colloquialism for trimming scissors), plastic turkey bags to hold the finished buds, and we went to work. After watching five movies back-to-back and working through the night, my father realised that the three pounds didn't need to be ready until the following week. But he told us he was proud of us, because we had learned a valuable life skill.

For those not in the know, 'trimming', 'table work', and other euphemistic terms refer to the practice of taking dried marijuana buds and cutting off the excess leaves and stems, ready for sale.

Trimmers usually stay at a grower's home, working all day long until the grower has no more product. In most cases trimmers are paid by the pound, ($200/lb being the standard in-season rate) unless their grow is weak. If that happens, you're paid by the hour, and the growers breathe down your neck to make sure you're churning the stuff out fast. I've heard horror stories of growers pacing back and forth toting rifles, but I was lucky – I only ever worked for family men.

In the fall of 2011, I took it up full time. Dad hooked me

up with the job at the beginning of October, and Mom drove me nine hours north to get there, for moral support. After quitting a job as sales associate at PacSun – actual hell for someone with my level of social anxiety – I was nervous about working again.

My first employers, Juan and Moira, lived on top of a mountain with no neighbours in any direction. They had a ten-month-old baby, Vision. When I first walked into their home on a foggy morning, Moira took one look at me and said, 'I'm sorry, but exactly how old are you?' I told her I was eighteen, and she sighed in relief. People always told her that she looked younger than she was, as well, she said.

Juan liked asking questions too.

'Right now, what would you say is the most addictive drug in the world?' There was a glint in his eye; I could tell this was going to be a series of trick questions, and I hated talking to people.

'Um, cocaine?'

'Nope. Guess again.'

'...Heroin?'

'Nuh-uh.' I paused, waiting. He flapped his hands. 'Come on, keep going.'

'Ecstasy?'

He raised his finger in the air and leaned into me.

'Sugar. The most addictive drug on this very earth... is sugar.'

'Oh really?' I feigned amazement.

'Yes, ma'am. The *real* white devil.'

I was ushered into an alcove off the kitchen overlooking the ridge, where Jill, the trim captain, was working away, nearly a pound already collected in the turkey bag by her feet. She was a tiny, thin woman who left the room every hour for a smoke break. She was '45 and proud of it'; I'd assumed she was nearing 60.

Jill graciously showed me the precise way to trim the

buds: the best fiskar angle, how tight to trim, and to make sure the stem was cut nice and flat. I wasn't much for conversation, so to fill the silence Jill put on oldies from her Internet radio. She was a career trimmer; she flew down from Washington every harvest and worked to keep herself and her trailer on her parents' property for the next year. Her parents were old, so when she told them she went to California to 'clean mansions for the stars to get them ready for the holidays,' they thought nothing of it.

Erica, another mom and friend of Moira's, arrived with her year-old son, Zen Meadow, in tow. Originally, Erica had planned to trim with the rest of us, but instead constantly complained, ate everything and smoked out Moira and Juan's weed. Zen Meadow was a crier who constantly badgered his mother for her THC-laced milk and screamed when denied it. Vision became so annoyed that he started hitting Zen Meadow when he cried, prompting baby battles that made Moira more edgy than she already was.

Moira loved cooking for us. The others said I was lucky; some growers fed their workers rice and beans, but I was a notoriously picky eater, and wasn't very grateful. All Moira's food was gluten-free. Her recipe for lasagna consisted of a layer of gluten and wheat-free pasta, kale, pasta, more kale, pasta, and a sprinkle of goat cheese on top – all *sans* sauce. I brought my own lunch the first few days until Moira told me there was plenty of food for everyone. The other trimmers glanced up from their work, fingers clipping away. I hesitated. Moira glared. 'Unless, you don't *like* my cooking, that is.'

Over the next month I learned how to swallow whole bites without choking.

After I left Juan and Moira's, I moved on to Jason's, the head of the Youth Shakespeare theater company in town. He was young and one of the town's most influential figures. A few years before, he'd been moving some pounds when the market was high. He arrived at the agreed parking lot, and waited for the guy to show. After twenty minutes, a black van pulled up and five guys hopped out, carrying baseball bats. They beat him to a pulp, took his stuff and drove off. They broke most of his ribs, a kneecap, the bones in his arms, and knocked out a few of his teeth. What was he going to do? He couldn't call the police and say, *Hey, some guys beat me up and stole all of my drugs!*

One of Jason's trimmers was older than the rest, and I recognized him. It turned out he was the son of someone my dad built a house for, some years earlier, and a paramedic. He asked me what I was doing with my life, and when I told him that I was starting college soon, he spent the next two hours telling me 'with all due respect' how college was a racket and that the only real way to go in life was to learn a trade or join the service. I nodded energetically.

Jason's business partner was a guy named Chad, forty-something with shoulder-length, wavy red hair. My dad told me he had just returned from touring Europe as an independent musician and considered himself a pretty cool guy. On my second day, Chad came into the basement and lowered himself down to my level, away from the rest of the group.

'Hey, how you doin' there?' he asked. I tried to keep my face calm, but being talked to one-on-one by the boss was never a good sign.

'I'm good,' I muttered, and stopped work. He picked up a large bud.

'See this here? What you're doing here is a r-e-e-a-a-l nice indoor trim.' He looked up and smiled. 'You're really good at that. But this is outdoor, so you just need to loosen it up.' He threw the bud in my bag and patted my thigh. 'Just loosen it up, that's all.'

I stared at the velvet Bob Marley portrait on the wall,

trying not to panic. He was nice about it – condescending, but nice. What he'd actually told me was that I'd fucked up big time. When you trim too tight, you're making less weight, and that makes the growers lose money. When you make them lose money, you lose their trust, and you probably won't be hired again.

I spent the next five hours constantly looking at everyone else's work, barely able to tell the difference between the trimmed and untrimmed piles. To compensate I cherry-picked the shit out of that bin (the highly discouraged practice of grabbing the biggest buds for yourself and leaving the small, light stuff for everyone else). I took all the fist-sized buds I could find, cut off the stems, and threw them in my bag.

At the end of the stay, I'd made $600 in five days. My job at PacSun had earned me $82.43 per week, after taxes. It would have taken me over seven weeks to make the same amount and I'd only had one panic attack. And it turns out I was doing so well, Jason and Chad paid for a round-trip flight to return after a week off.

I had found my new employment.

The only drawback was that I couldn't tell my LA friends about my new livelihood. I made up for the secrecy with potent, quarter-filled sandwich baggies of hash for Christmas.

SCREENPLAYS*

* Standard screenplay formatting has
been adjusted to book's size and style

DOBY'S GONE
(BASED ON THE SHORT STORY 'DOBY'S GONE'
BY ANN PETRY)
Omari Swanston-Jeffers

MONTAGE

ARCHIVE FOOTAGE

– WW2. 'England needs you', the war effort, West Indians enlist and fight in British armed forces.

– Postwar. Tilbury Dock, Essex. West Indian servicemen step off the boat and onto British shores.

– Dances. West-Indian servicemen dance with English women, some British servicemen join in, others stand off.

– 1950s. The economic boom. Streams of West Indian families flood off the ships.

– 1960s. Industrial reality. Cold, belching chimneys, poverty, placards 'KEEP BRITAIN WHITE' 'NO BLACKS, NO DOGS, NO IRISH', Teddy boys.

EXT. LIVERPOOL DOCKS, IMMIGRATION CONTROL – DAY

Insert caption: Liverpool, Winter 1965

From the perspective of SUE (6). Her small hands wrapped in colourful mittens. Her left hand clutches a lady's gloved hand; her right hand holds onto a big, gloved male hand.

Below, murky dock water. High above, a steel ceiling where pigeons flutter and hide in archways.

As we start to move, Sue's focus drops in and out of her sur-roundings; she notices the queues, hundreds of smartly dressed, towering people, shivering in the cold.

EXT. DOCK ENTRANCE/EXIT/STREETS – DAY

Still through Sue's eyes. England is a cold, white wonder-land. Frost crisps roads and pavements into glittering dia-monds.

Tall chimneys breathe black, sooty smoke.

Walking on down a high street, past a sweet shop. Stop. Go back.

Now, reflected in the shop window, we see Sue – a little black girl with big hair, carrying a suitcase and holding her mother's hand. MRS JOHNSON – a smartly dressed West In-dian lady, also carrying a suitcase.

England – the perspective of Mrs Johnson – is grey and bleak.

Back to Sue's perspective. The other hand is in DOBY's – Sue's imaginary friend, a big white male skinhead. Doby's painted in blue body paint; his arms are covered by purple fur; he wears a white vest, gloves, a purple tutu, blue tights and biker boots. And he carries Sue's suitcase.

In the road a taxi passes. Mrs Johnson flags it down.

INT. TRAIN – DAY SERIES OF SHOTS

A British Rail second-class carriage in off-peak hours, a mixed racial and social bag of passengers.

Sue, Doby and Mrs Johnson sit at a table seat: Sue next to the window; Mrs Johnson in the aisle seat. From Sue's perspective we see Doby occupying the seat between them.

As we travel, the ethnic and social diversity wanes; passengers become more white, more middle class.

Passengers get on and off the train; the seats opposite the Johnsons fill. The carriage fills.

A BUSINESSMAN approaches. From his perspective there's an empty seat between Sue and her mother. Sue looks alarmed – Doby's sitting right there. She tugs her mother's sleeve. Mrs Johnson gestures that the seat's taken. The Businessman grunts then, politely, storms off.

Sue sleeps against Doby's shoulder. A uniformed black TICKET INSPECTOR checks Mrs Johnson's tickets. Sue wakes. She looks at the Ticket Inspector in awe.

EXT. YORK STATION – NIGHT

MR JOHNSON, a handsome West Indian dressed in overalls, waits, smoking a pipe and leaning against a Bedford truck.

In the cab, a black WORKMATE waits at the wheel, listening to a transistor radio.

Mrs Johnson and Sue arrive. Mr Johnson runs toward them. Sue runs to her Daddy. Mrs Johnson watches, smiling.

                    SUE
         Daddy!

Mr Johnson swings Sue up and around and into his arms.

INT. BEDFORD TRUCK – NIGHT

The truck heads 'home', Workmate at the wheel, Mr Johnson in front seat and, in the rear, Sue and Mrs Johnson with Doby sits between.

As the Workmate glances in the rear view mirror we see an empty space between Sue and her mother.

Sue looks at the nightscape of York where pavements glisten and sparkle in the rain.

Mrs Johnson looks at the nightscape of York where ice rain pours.

Sue sees pretty houses and gardens.

Mrs Johnson sees run-down terraces and race-hate placards.

                WORKMATE
         How the trip go, Mrs Johnson?

                    SUE
         Ohh, look Doby, look!

                MRS JOHNSON
         We lef' St' Kits an' sail six days, until we reach
         Tenerife, where we stock on fruit an' thing.
         Next we reach Spain, an' the people were beggin'.

MR JOHNSON
So, sweetheart, wha'yu think of the Mother
country 'den?

SUE
See the fireflies Doby? They follow us. They
light the streets. How you think them know
to stay up such straight lines? ...You don't
know? Mi' na' know either...

MR JOHNSON (CONT'D)
Boy, mi' never think I woulda see a pauper outside
a di West Indies.

EXT. THORNTON LE DALE – EARLY HOURS

Even at night we can see this is a picture-postcard Dales village.

The Bedford truck pulls up outside Sue's new home – a
small terraced house. Mr Johnson jumps out, grabs the suit-
cases and holds the door for his wife, and lifts his daughter
down.

MR JOHNSON
Welcome home mi' darlings.

Mrs Johnson and Sue stand, looking at their new home.
Doby slips out of the truck before the Workmate slams the
door.

WORKMATE
So mi' pick you up in the morning.

MR JOHNSON
Yes Sir! Just as the sun a'rise.

Doby shelters on the doorstep. Sue joins him.

> SUE
> This is our home now Doby.

INT. HOME – EARLY HOURS

Mr Johnson carries Sue, her arms are wrapped around his neck. His free hand holds Mrs Johnson's. They move through the house – more a man's crash pad than a family home...

INT. SUE'S ROOM – CONTINUOUS

...into Sue's newly painted bedroom. On the walls are photos of Sue's birthdays. The first two picture a 'perfect family', the subsequent four lack Mr Johnson. Sue looks at an armchair by the bed.

> SUE
> Doby sleep there.

Mr Johnson's confused. Mrs Johnson nods to the door.

> MRS JOHNSON
> And us?

Mr Johnson puts his arm round her and leads her away.

Sue unpacks her things. First out are her drawings. They echo the photos but with Doby in all of them where Mr Johnson should be.

INT. SUE'S ROOM – DAY

Mrs Johnson, dressed in nurse's uniform, comes in to wake

Sue. Sue's already awake, playing with (invisible) Doby.

MONTAGE – MORNING ROUTINE
A) INT. BATHROOM – Sue and Doby in a bath at opposite ends. They splash each other, while Mrs Johnson bathes Sue.

B) INT. SUE'S BEDROOM – Mrs Johnson helps Sue get dressed in her new school uniform: white blouse, a burgundy jumper, a red-white plaid skirt, and – Sue's choosing – bright orange high socks. Doby dons a red-white plaid shirt to match Sue's skirt.

C) INT. MRS JOHNSON'S ROOM – Mrs Johnson tames Sue's wild hair into braids. Doby adds red hair ribbons.

INT. KITCHEN – CONTINUOUS

At table, Sue eats breakfast, beside her an empty place.

> SUE
> ...Doby have a pencil, and him got a shirt jus' like mi' dress.

> MRS JOHNSON
> Why can't Doby stay home?

Doby appears, puts his plate of imaginary food on the table.

> SUE
> Because, him go everywhere mi' go...

Breakfast finished, Sue and Doby don matching winter coats.

> MRS JOHNSON
> And where do you think yu' a'go young lady?

SUE
To school Mama, me and Doby. Look.

Mrs Johnson gives Sue a look. 'The Look'.

SUE (CONT'D)
You a'come with mi', Mamma?

MRS JOHNSON
Stop yu' nonsense mi' a'come. Mi' need to
speak with yu' teacher.

Sue looks down and frowns.

EXT. STREET – LATER

Sue – with Doby in the middle – and Mrs Johnson hold hands
as they walk. School is visible at the end of the road.

Through Mrs Johnson's eyes, the journey appears short.

Through Sue's eyes, the street is long, the school distant.

EXT. SCHOOL PLAYGROUND – CONTINUOUS

The school is a small brick building. CHILDREN play outside.
Mrs Johnson leads the way through the playground, Sue
trails behind, staring at the Children staring at her.

SUE
Why them a'look at me so hard?

MRS JOHNSON
Probably 'cus yu' a'look them so.

INT. CLASSROOM – CONTINUOUS

The classroom is child-friendly, bright walls plastered with posters and children's work. MONDAY is written in chalk on a blackboard. The classroom clock reads 8:45.

MISS WHITTIER (30s) – white skin, curly yellow hair, purple dress, purple shoes and purple head band – at the teacher's desk, talking to Mrs Johnson.

Sue looks round the empty class. She tries to focus on her mother and teacher, but floats off into her own world.

>   MRS JOHNSON
> I need to talk about my daughter's 'friend' –

>   SUE
>   (to invisible Doby)
> – you think teacher will sit you by me? I don't know either.

Miss Whittier looks at Sue, talking to (invisible) Doby.

>   MISS WHITTIER
> Why don't you go and play, Sue?

>   SUE
> Yes, teacher.

>   MISS WHITTIER
> You can call me Miss Whittier.

>   SUE
> Yes, Miss Whittier.

Dragging Doby with her, Sue heads out.

EXT. SCHOOL PLAYGROUND – CONTINUOUS

Sue and Doby look round the playground.

Children skipping, playing hopscotch, football, tag.

Sue's eyes light up when she sees the hopscotch, but Doby hangs back.

>   SUE
>   Come on, hold my hand!

Hand in hand, Sue and Doby cross the playground. Without stopping play, Children stare. Sue stops by the hopscotch.

>   SUE (CONT'D)
>   Can we play too?

JIMMIE PIEBALD, red hair, frowns.

Doby's hiding behind Sue but his shadow is visible.

Jimmie shakes his head. DAISY BELL, freckled, sticks her tongue out at Sue. Children continue playing. Jimmie looks at Sue.

>   JIMMIE PIEBALD
>   Your legs are black.

>   CHILD I
>   She's black all over!

Doby pulls back. Sue retreats. Children follow them.

> DAISY BELL
> Look, look. Her legs are black!

Children form a ring. They dance up and down.

> CHILDREN
> HER LEGS ARE BLACK! HER LEGS ARE BLACK...

Sue shrinks. Doby towers above everyone, but does nothing.
From the Children's perspective, Sue talks to thin air.

> SUE
> What do they mean Doby? They're not black,
> they're brown. Just like theirs're pink not
> white. Some children are dark and some are
> light – Mama said so...

The BELL rings. Forgetting Sue, Children form lines, ready to
go inside.

INT. CLASSROOM – MINUTES LATER

Sue and Doby enter the classroom. The desks are full. Jimmie
and Daisy near the back. Walls no longer seem bright.

> SUE
> Don't you mind, Doby. Don't you mind.
> I won't let them hurt you.

Miss Whittier shows Sue a seat at the front. An encouraging
smile. Sue tries to smile back, but tears sting her eyes. Doby,
nowhere to sit, stands at the front of the class. Sue tugs his
sleeve, pulling him close to her seat.

SUE (CONT'D)
Yu' stand right close to me an' if yu' get
tired, just sit right here.

Points to edge of seat.

INT. CLASSROOM – DAY

Children's VOICES at play outside. Quiet inside. The clock
shows 11:00, Tuesday chalked on the blackboard.

Sue sits at her desk. Her socks are a sad shade of blue, hair in
corn rows, no ribbons. She watches Children through a window. Doby stands by the seat, like yesterday.

Miss Whittier, matching purple blouse and skirt, puts equipment back in a cupboard, goes to the blackboard to prep the
next lesson.

MISS WHITTIER
Why don't you come help me Sue.

Sue comes to the blackboard. Miss Whittier draws flowers
and Sue colours them. As they draw, Sue cups her hands and
whispers to Doby.

SUE
I love mi' teacher, Doby. I love Miss Whittier,
mi' teacher.

EXT. SCHOOL PLAYGROUND – DAY

End of school bell RINGS. Children stream out of the school,
across the playground and home.

Sue's socks are a cowardly yellow. Ribbons in, her hair is scraped tight across her scalp, wild bunches at each side. She falls into step with Jimmie and Daisy who run off, laughing.

Sue doesn't know whether to run after them. Doby pulls her back.

EXT. STREET – LATER

A group of BOYS lie in wait behind a wall. Jimmie is among them.

Sue walks home. We don't see Doby, but his large shadow is next to hers.

The Boys jump out from behind the wall. Sue's startled.

> BOY 2
> Look she's scared! Want to run?

> BOY 1
> That's all you Wogs are good at.

> GROUP
> RUN GOLLIWOG, RUN! – RUN GOLLIWOG!

Jimmie grabs a stick. The Boys chase. Sue and Doby are forced to run.

> SUE
> Faster, Doby! Yu' must go faster!

EXT. HOME – FRONT PORCH – MOMENTS LATER

From the perspective of MISS SNOW – an elderly white neighbour, dressed in black – Sue arrives panting. No one's at home. In tears, Sue sits on the doorstep.

> MISS SNOW
> Oh my dear, what is wrong?

Sue, struggling to catch her breath, pants as she speaks.

> SUE
> Mi all-right Missis. But I don't think Doby happy.

> MS SNOW
> Why not?

> SUE
> I don't think him like other children-them.

EXT. STREET – DAY

Sue walks to school on her own. Today her hair is semi-out; two red ribbons wrap two bundles of curls. Her socks are striped pink and purple.

INT. CLASSROOM – CONTINUOUS

The blackboard reads THURSDAY. The clock shows 2.30.

Doby's at the back of the class, in the back of Sue's mind.

Again in purple, Miss Whittier talks to her pupils.

> MISS WHITTIER
> Can anyone name the first vowel?

Children raise their hands. Miss Whittier points at Sue.

> SUE
> Is it A, Miss Whittier?

INT. CLASSROOM – DAY

The blackboard reads 'FRIDAY'. The clock ticks to 3:00.

Sue's hair is a wild, wavy Afro, bright red ribbons hanging loose, bright red socks. Sue is daydreaming – the class is filled with imaginary creatures, including a purple princess sitting on top of her desk.

EXT. SCHOOL GATES/STREET – LATER

Lost in her own world, Sue and Doby start home. They don't see the group of Children waiting behind the wall, Daisy and Jimmie at the back of the group.

> CHILD I
> How do you comb that hair?

> BOY I
> Does that black wash off?

> CHILDREN
> HER LEGS ARE BLACK! HER LEGS ARE BLACK!
> HER LEGS ARE BLACK!

A GIRL snatches at Sue's hair. One of the red ribbons comes loose. Sue tries to catch it. Children close on her. A child pushes her. Sue tumbles. Doby remains rooted to the spot.

> JIMMIE PIEBALD
> My mum says you're a little nigger.

That's it! Sue rises, plants her feet firm in the ground. She throws out her fist. She starts hitting, kicking, pulling hair, tearing at clothes.

Sue reaches down, grabs a fist full of gravel, chucks it.

Dust envelops her. The dust transforms into a cloud of glittery purple mist. Slow, the mist cloud settles.

Children scatter and run.

Sue stands fierce. She looks round for Doby, realises he's gone...

> SUE
> Doby... Doby?

She looks in all directions, listens. Nothing.

> SUE (CONT'D)
> Doby! Doby! Doby! Where are you?

But Doby is nowhere to be seen.

Sue checks herself. Her dress is torn, she's scratched all over, socks round her ankles, both red ribbons gone.

Sue looks down at her legs. We see her shadow grow. The legs grow longer, like her father from the birthday pictures. Sue stares at her shadow, as she moves it moves.

Daisy Bell appears from the spot where Doby disappeared.

> DAISY BELL
> Do you want to walk home together?

EXT. STREET/FIELD/WELL – CONTINUOUS

Sue and Daisy walk along the street. Jimmie Piebald trails up behind them, falls in alongside them. The three walk in silence.

A field opens up to one side of the street. They look at each other, then run – race.

They stop at a well, look into it, HOLLER into it, listening to their voices ECHO. Then LAUGH.

EXT. HOME – FRONT PORCH – CONTINUOUS

The sun is setting. Daisy and Jimmie walk Sue home. Mrs Johnson is waiting.

> MRS JOHNSON
> Sue! Whe' yu' been? What happen to –

Daisy Bell puts her arm around Sue. Jimmie kicks at stones. Sue looks to her left, trying to remember what it is, who it is. Then she does.

> SUE
> Doby gone. Mi cah find him anywhere.

THE END

BIRTHDAY PARTY
Tova Naslund

INT. LIVING ROOM – DAY

Squeals of childish delight.

The room's decorated with bunting and shiny balloons spelling Happy Birthday.

Half a dozen KIDS (5 to 6) sit cross-legged in a circle, enthralled by an AUGUSTE CLOWN in full costume and red make-up, fashioning weird and wonderful animals out of balloons.

The Clown ties the last knot and passes a pink piggy balloon to the BIRTHDAY GIRL (5). Kids CLAMOUR for their balloons.

INT. KITCHEN – DAY

Kids' VOICES just as loud in here. DAD (30s) arranges five candles on a birthday cake. MUM (30s) stands guard at the living room door, to make sure no one sees the cake yet.

> MUM
> They love him.

> DAD
> Sounds like it.

Dad strikes a match and lights the candles. The cake

sparkles as he lifts it up.

     DAD (CONT'D)
Get the lights, will you.

Mum reaches round the door for the living room light switch.

     MUM
Where did you find him?

     DAD
I didn't. I thought you did.

Kids' SCREAMS from the living room.

THE END

STARE

George Ross

EXT. HOUSE – NIGHT

A large, dilapidated country house in the moonlight. No lights in the house apart from a pink glow from an attic.

INT. BEDROOM – NIGHT

Moonbeams slant into a small girl's bedroom, mixing with the pink night light by the bedside, and making toy fairies scattered on the floor sparkle.

A GIRL (5) – short hair, bright eyes, sugar-plum nightie – sits up in bed, staring at an old-fashioned wardrobe.

The wardrobe door CREAKS.

Girl grips the fairy-print duvet.

A GROWL

The Girl stares at a purple-clawed hand emerging from the wardrobe. Green eyes stare back at her from inside the wardrobe. A CREATURE crouches behind the wardrobe door.

The Girl stares. The Creature stares back. The Girl stares hard. The Creature stares harder. They stare at one another, more and more intense.

The intensity reaches its climax. The Creature blinks. The Girl grins.

                    GIRL
        You blinked first!

The Creature comes out – a fat, ugly, purple, wild-boar monster, with little rubbery horns.

                    CREATURE
        Ah fuck!

The Creature retreats into the wardrobe and SLAMS the door.

THE END

NOWHERE

Patrick Hawkes

INT. BEDROOM – NIGHT

Distant SIRENS and TRAFFIC.

Orange light from a street lamp filters through an ill-fitting sash window beaded with condensation, into a grotty bedroom, stuffed with dilapidated 70s furniture.

JOHN and TONY (late and early 20s) lie naked and awkward in a single bed, bottom halves covered by a thin sheet.

John – tall, toned and tanned, head shaved, beard and chest stubbly – lies on his back, eyes open, face expressionless, staring at ceiling.

Tony, a pony-tailed waif, curls against John, head on his chest, eyes open, face expressionless.

Sirens and traffic stop.

Silence.

Quickly, awkwardly, Tony takes his chance.

> TONY
> Love you.

John stares at ceiling.

Silence.

Tony's eyes wide, waiting. John stares at the ceiling.

A car HORN SOUNDS. SIRENS and TRAFFIC respond.

John stares at the ceiling.

Tony closes his eyes.

THE END

LOST DUCKLING

Rob Heimann

EXT. CANAL BRIDGE – DAY

A canal and towpath sparkle in the morning light.

A tattooed SKINHEAD – Doc Martins, combats, and a black T – swaggers over a canal bridge.

A FEMALE JOGGER swerves wide as she passes him. Without breaking his stride, he turns and spits after her.

EXT. TOWPATH – DAY

A lone DUCKLING peers out from undergrowth by the towpath. A discarded cigarette packet in the grass THRUMS as Doc Martins approach.

> DUCKLING
> Cheep.

Doc Martins stop by the undergrowth. The Skinhead squats down, picks out the cigarette packet, parts the grass and stares at the Duckling.

The Skinhead straightens up, chucks the cigarette packet into the canal and glances up and down the towpath, checking to see if anyone's coming around. No one. He squats again.

SKINHEAD
You lost?

DUCKLING
Cheep.

The Skinhead scoops up the Duckling, holds it to his chest making CLUCKING noises.

SKINHEAD
Let's see if we can find your mum.

THE END

MAMIHLAPINAPATAI
Saskia Mears

INT. LIVING ROOM – NIGHT

A darkened room. A sofa. Pizza boxes everywhere, uneaten pizza crusts mixed with DVD cases litter the floor.

On the sofa, YOUNG MAN and a YOUNG WOMAN (both 20-ish), zipped up to their chins in separate sleeping bags, her at the back, him at the front, trying not to touch.

On the sofa arm, a phone BUZZES on silent and lights up. Young Man unzips his bag, extracts one hand and tries to grab the phone without touching Young Woman.

But his hand brushes the back of her shoulder. She tenses. He snatches his hand away.

They look at each other, then away. She holds still, he fidgets. Another glance. A quick smile.

Still zipped in her bag, she wriggles along the sofa until she's facing him, eye to eye.

He goes to speak just as she does. They stop, both nervous. He laughs. She panics.

> YOUNG WOMAN
> I need the loo.

ZIP. She's out of her sleeping bag. ZIP. He sits up to let her pass. She touches him as she shimmies over him and disappears.

He pulls a sofa cushion over his head in frustration.

THE END

YELLOW VELVET
(BASED ON 'BREATHING', A SHORT STORY BY LEONE ROSS)
Jenna Redah

INT. KITCHEN – DAY

A kettle RUMBLES to the boil.

A man's hands rifle through an open cupboard, pushing aside slim waist and detox teas until they reach a box of Tetley tea bags.

PATRICK SNYDER (43), green pyjamas, grey face, dangles a tea bag as he looks for a cup.

Open cereal boxes. Dried jam on butcher knives. Crumbs on counter tops. Unwashed dishes in a grimy sink.

Steam rises. Kettle CLICKS.

Patrick grabs a mug of moulded tea off a table by the window, beyond which we glimpse a snow-covered garden.

Patrick upends the mug over the sink, spewing out old tea. He plops the new tea bag into the cup and pours on boiling water.

INT. LIVING ROOM – DAY

Exposed brick walls. Patrick, cradling his tea mug, lies on a sofa marooned in the middle of an empty room, staring blankly at a blank TV screen.

One foot starts tapping. Patrick glances at the four walls, his head snapping between them. Faster, faster. His foot ups the tempo. Head tries to keep time.

Enough.

Patrick leaps off the sofa, spilling tea down his green pyjamas.

INT. KITCHEN – EVENING

Purple sky and fresh snowfall through the window.

Patrick, brown pyjamas, sits at the table writing. Two slices of toast and a steaming mug of tea untouched to one side. To the other, a leather journal open on the last page, full of black biro notes, resting on top of an identical closed journal.

Patrick opens a new journal, picks up the black biro and writes "22nd Cycle" in the top corner of the first page.

INT. BEDROOM – NIGHT

A naked long-life bulb casts long shadows across the room.

Male clothes in hues of dark green, brown and maroon are folded neatly on the floor. Pearl necklace rests on top.

Digital clock on a bedside table reads 01:28.

On a double bed Patrick, green pyjamas melting into a for-

est-green bedspread, stares vacantly at the ceiling. Mastur-
bates.

INT. BEDROOM – LATER

Clock reads 4:59.

Patrick, topless, stomach bulging over green pyjama bot-
toms, does tricep curls with dumbbells.

Clock clicks to 5:00.

A doorbell RINGS.

Dumbbells THUD to the floor.

Patrick creeps over to the light switch. FLICK. Light out.

Yellow streetlight through crumpled curtains.

Patrick crawls to the window, raises his head to sill height
and peers out.

A porch obstructs his view of a FIGURE standing in the snow.

Patrick raises his head higher.

The Figure leans toward the porch. The doorbell RINGS.

Patrick ducks.

INT. HOUSE DOORWAY – MINUTES LATER

Patrick flattens himself against the wall by the door, hand
creeping toward the doorknob.

The doorbell RINGS. A fist POUNDS the door.

Patrick throws the door open. Porch light turns on, revealing LULU AWAD (19), thick eyebrows, curls to her waist, and draped in a white sheet that's muddy against the newly fallen snow.

Patrick slams the door shut. Pauses. Opens the door.

> LULU
> Either you let me in, or I'll leave.

> PATRICK
> You're...

> LULU
> Okay, bye –

She turns. Patrick pulls her inside and kisses her.

INT. BEDROOM – SUNRISE

Patrick and Lulu naked on the ivory bedspread, both out of breath.

The bedroom's had a make over – eggshell French cupboards, a vanity table, make up, powder, glass perfume bottles, Cognac, pearls, crisp curtains drawn shut.

Patrick tries to kiss Lulu.

> PATRICK
> Missed you.

She pushes him away.

LULU
You know what that makes you?

PATRICK
God'll forgive me.

LULU
Don't talk to me about God.

PATRICK
Don't leave me again. Don't do that.

He grips Lulu.

LULU
After all my prayers, all the mosques,
He still gave me a hard time.

PATRICK
Did he burn Baby?

Patrick's fingers follow the green and blue of Lulu's inner arms. His eyes caress her collarbone, her breasts, the grooves between her ribs. His fingers trace each rib, counting, one at a time – true rib, false rib – until they reach and inspect her floating ribs.

LULU
Get off me! The tyre tracks have gone and hell's
not how they say in the Quran or the Bible –

PATRICK
You're safe now.

Patrick pulls her back to him. Kisses her open mouth.

> LULU
> It's not fire, there's no burning. It's like, your worst
> nightmare over and over with variations and –

> PATRICK
> I won't let you leave again.

They lie in silence. Lulu examines her hand.

> LULU
> What am I?

> PATRICK
> I don't care. You're back. That's all.

Lulu kicks Patrick away and tumbles out of bed.

> LULU
> I need to find out!

She clambers to her feet, grabs her grubby sheet and is gone.

INT. KITCHEN – MOMENTS LATER

Sunrise glints through the window, giving a golden glow to
a spotless kitchen, cream tiles and corn-silk surfaces.

Patrick, in Burgundy dressing gown, finds Lulu, wrapped in
her grubby sheet standing at the sink, cutting at her hand
with the butcher's knife.

> PATRICK
> Stop it! Lulu! Stop it!

He snatches the knife and throws it into the sink.

>   PATRICK (CONT'D)
> For fuck's sake. What have you done?

Lulu holds up her hand. Her forearm runs red. There are splatter patterns on the sheet.

>   LULU
> Look! A fountain.

>   PATRICK
> Listen to me –

>   LULU
> I can't feel the cut. Maybe I'm a superhero.
> Can we try you?

>   PATRICK
> No!

Lulu retrieves the knife and swipes. Patrick gasps and draws his arm back, inspecting the cut.

>   LULU
> God, I'm sorry.

Lulu peers at Patrick's wound, matter of fact.

>   LULU (CONT'D)
> It's not bleeding. Maybe I didn't cut deep
> enough. Let me try again –

She slices at him with the knife, Patrick slaps her away, sending the knife spinning across the floor.

Lulu watches it settle. Patrick kicks it under the counter, where she can't reach it. Lulu sulks.

> PATRICK
> Don't touch anything.

Patrick goes.

Lulu stands, clenching and unclenching her fist, watching how it affects the blood.

INT. KITCHEN – MINUTES LATER

Lulu, wearing a yellow velvet nightdress, sits at the table reading Patrick's journals.

Patrick, returning with a green first-aid kit, clocks this.

> PATRICK
> Lu?

> LULU
> What is this?

Patrick concentrates on the first-aid kit, opens it up, selects a bandage.

> LULU (CONT'D)
> Answer me!

> PATRICK
> Don't raise your voice at me.

> LULU
> What are these? Fantasies? Dreams? Why

would you write this?

Patrick abandons first aid and turns to the stove, back to her.

> PATRICK
> Do you want breakfast?

> LULU
> Don't you turn away from me! I want to know
> why you've filled journals with me dying over
> and over –

Lulu waves his journal in the air.

> LULU (CONT'D)
> You saw it coming. You could have pushed me
> out of the way, but you didn't, did you?

Patrick can't face her.

> LULU (CONT'D)
> Coward.

> PATRICK
> Baby girl, I swear. I swear. I reached out, I tried –

> LULU
> You tried just enough to save yourself. Tell me
> how that worked out?

She tosses the journal onto the table. Patrick tries to mollify
her.

> PATRICK
> I was upset. I was angry. I blamed myself –

>   LULU
> It's funny. It hit us both anyway, now I'm
> the one alive and you're dead.

>   PATRICK
> I fucking exaggerated what I wrote! Everyone
> feels guilty when someone dies.

Lulu doesn't buy it. She glances at the door. Patrick's between her and it.

>   PATRICK (CONT'D)
> Come here.

He takes the bandage from the first-aid kit.

>   PATRICK (CONT'D)
> You're still dripping blood.

He reaches for her hand, she pulls away, eyes on door.

>   LULU
> I need to go.

>   PATRICK
> No.

>   LULU
> I'm leaving.

Lulu makes it to the door. Patrick grabs her. She slaps him. He punches her. She falls.

>   PATRICK
> Lulu, don't.

He stands over her. Lulu's hand reaches across the floor for the butcher's knife.

>   PATRICK (CONT'D)
>   Don't.

Patrick's straddling her now, clawing the knife away, spinning it out of her reach.

Patrick's hands around Lulu's throat. Patrick watches them squeeze her windpipe. It bulges. Lulu thrashes. Kicks. Chokes. Falls still.

Patrick on the floor, watching Lulu.

Silence.

There's a dirty mug on the floor. Patrick reaches over, picks it up. Stands up and places it in the sink with all the dirty dishes.

He steps over Lulu to get to the kettle. CLICKS it on and looks round.

Kitchen's littered with open cereal boxes. Dried jam on butcher knives. Crumbs on counter tops. Mugs of moulded tea on a table by the window, snowy garden beyond.

Patrick opens a cupboard. Shoves fancy teas aside to reach the Tetley.

THE END

NOVEL EXTRACTS

TO SPITE THE WEEVIL
Nanou Blair Gould

1

The apple sat on the table in the shape of an apple. There was nothing more to it than that. I'd thought otherwise but when I bit into it, the flesh dissolved like bubble bath in my mouth.

It was a bad apple.

It was just an apple.

2

For no particular reason, I'm thinking about Mike Weevil. Mike was my dad's colleague who died. I'd say I think more about Mike Weevil than Dad does, though I don't think anyone knows that. I never met him and he died when I was six.

My name is Evie Appleton. I know that doesn't paint a picture. I know three Evies off the top of my head: Evie Lewis, a friend I met at ballet when I was five. Evie Phats, or Fat Evie, who was in the year above and who works at Waitrose and who will always work at Waitrose, according to Mr Phelps our maths tutor, because she's ASDA material and is punching above her belt.

Evie Crab lives on my road. She used to have waist length white-blonde hair that she wore in plaits. Once she asked whether we could be best friends because of our names. I said no, because I didn't like that anyone else had my name. She said, not Evie: Apple, like her uncle's pub in

Cornwall, The Crab and Apple. I still said no. I got jealous of girls with hair longer than mine. When Mike Weevil died, I was doodling with scented gel pens so I couldn't smell the beer on Dad, but I knew he smelled of beer because my 10 year-old brother Barney said he did. Oh Christ, said Mum, You've been fired. Dad said, No, no. Actually Mike Weevil died. Mum groaned. He was only forty-odd, she said and Dad said, I know. He went and topped himself.

That means he killed himself, Barney told me. I had never known anyone to die, let alone kill themselves. I was fascinated. Dad took his time. He sat down beside me. He put an arm on the back of my chair.

You know how you're sometimes frightened of dying? he said.

And I said yes.

Well, Mike got frightened a lot. So much, in fact, that he was never not frightened.

He held my gaze. I held his, expectantly. Dad sighed and said, So he ended his suffering himself.

I said: Mike Weevil killed himself because he was scared of dying.

I looked at Barney and he looked at me and we both burst out laughing. It was the most stupid thing I'd ever heard. I'm not a bully. I never was, but I felt such contempt for the man with little eyes and a goofy smile in the obituary Mum showed me. Barney told me a weevil is a type of beetle. I liked that. I imagined Mike scuttling under my foot with his little beetle body because he was afraid I'd squash him when he wasn't looking. Later I fished the obituary from the bin to pore over his picture again.

No one ever told me how Mike killed himself. Or if they did I've forgotten and haven't asked since. The only way I could forgive Mike for his suicide was to think of it as clever: Mike Weevil cheated his own death. Because people who are scared of death aren't so scared of dying but of not knowing when they're going to stop living. Mike Weevil packed forty-six years worth of adrenaline into that last moment, made his first impulsive decision as he crossed Waterloo Bridge on his way to work. He would have been shuffling along, thinking about death as usual, seen the sunrise over the Thames, and been filled with an idea so strong that he climbed onto the railings and dived head first into the churning river.

I don't notice twenty-one year old Barney come into the kitchen. I'm listening to the radio. I don't see him because I'm squinting at the hot yellow light thinking *the sun the sun the sun*, and of Mike Weevil as a quieter thought, until the light bulb burns green stains onto my eyeballs. I blink and Barney's standing there. He cuts the music.

'Have you been into the bathroom?' he asks. The rain drums against the double glazing, it splinters in the gutter.

'No,' I say.

'Can't you smell it?' he says. 'The sewage is coming up through the bath.'

'Oh *no*.'

'Oh yes,' says Barney.

He checks the cupboard beneath the kitchen sink. We've run out of sandbags. We bought seven, as many as we could carry between two of us, and we've run out. He sits down opposite me.

'We need more sandbags.'

'We could glue the plug in,' I suggest.

'The sewage would just come up through the toilet or sink.'

We hear the flop-thump of Boromir on the stairs. Barney gets up and a moment later he's back with the giant hare hanging in his arms. The fur on Boromir's belly is wet and Barney says, 'It's soaking into the carpet on the landing.'

'How can we drain it if there's nowhere to drain it?' I ask.

'We can't,' says Barney.

I don't believe in fate or destiny or even the weather

forecast, but they predicted rain, the rain came and now it won't stop. Our parents insisted London couldn't flood in five days. London flooded in five days. Not completely. Heathrow shut down on the eve of their return from Sicily five nights ago, and the flat bit of Loughborough Junction where we live is flooded. That much I know. Barney lugged the television set upstairs when the first water trickled under the front door and neither of us bothered setting it back up in one of the bedrooms. We make do with the radio for news, although once it's on we tend to switch it off again – too many doom and gloom reminders that it's still *raining*. We listen to music instead.

We drove out and bought sandbags and tarp sheets, bottles of water, baked beans, pasta, chocolate and beer, just in case we couldn't get out again. We had to go out again to move the car to a multi-storey car park. We heard people were doing that on the radio. Of course, being on the radio, everyone started moving their cars to multi-storey car parks. We drove for almost two hours trying to find a space and then waded all the way home because they'd closed the Underground.

The water somehow still runs clean and hot from the kitchen tap. I fill a bucket and upturn a bottle of antibac and we clatter upstairs with mops and buckets. It's not just the bath, it's the toilet too. The Borough's muck brimming to the rim. Barney shuts Boromir in his bedroom and with a cheery smile he lets me choose between bath and toilet.

I can barely look as he reaches into the loo with a plastic beaker. It's a disgusting job, one of the most disgusting things I've ever done. It's no use pulling my pyjama top over my nose, the stink seeps through the fabric, into my hair and skin. Barney scoops up something like a clump of hair but clotted yellow brown, which latches onto his wrist as he tries to shake it off and he retches so hard he hits his head on the toilet seat. I laugh so much I gulp mouthfuls of the vile air and have to run out to breath over the bannister.

Of course, we are just wasting energy because the toilet keeps refilling itself. We're at work for almost an hour before we accept that Lambeth's sewage is beyond Barney's beaker.

'If it comes down to it, I'm filling the loo with sand,' Barney says. We're leaning against the radiator. My skin and hair feel sticky and brittle. It clearly has come to it, so we carry the sloshing buckets downstairs to pour them out of the kitchen window. The clotted hairball dribbles over the lip of my bucket and I scream. Like a fat slug secreting its insides, it slides the length of the double glazing and out of sight.

In some perverse way, I'm enjoying myself. The job's so disgusting I'm distracted from the rain; although now I'm aware of *that*, I'm thinking about it again. I turn away from the window. Barney is dragging a sandbag from the front door. We carry it upstairs between us. I have to empty the sewage already collecting in the toilet bowl and rinse with hot, soapy water before Barney pours in the sand.

'This is *disgusting*,' Barney mutters.

'*So* disgusting,' I agree.

'We can't even have a shower,' says Barney.

'We're going to have to pee in the sink.'

We laugh helplessly.

'We could make ourselves a litter in here with the rest of the sand.'

'If it's good enough for Boromir, it's good enough for me.' Barney rubs his face again. When he looks at me his eyebrows and lashes are crumpled. I think he's about to smile. He doesn't bother. I don't either. We just look at each other and listen to the onslaught of water filling the country like the toilet bowl.

HOW TO DRINK COFFEE

Vera Sugar

The day was Thursday, the time just before six, when Mr Roger
Dandelion realised that he had nothing left to do.

He swallowed.

He had kept himself busy all day. As soon as he got to
his office, he turned on the computer and spent hours reading through fresh proposals – one about a lost kitten, one
about a hungry frog, and one about a tomato on a farm. He
liked the ideas, but the proposals were badly written, there-
fore forgettable. Mr Dandelion hesitated. It was his last day,
so he forwarded them all to the editor next door. Peter was
good at saying no in a polite manner. After that, he'd attended a staff meeting to update projects: a cookbook was
on hold, a book about a caterpillar was nearly finished. Two
new projects were coming in, and they seemed to be in good
hands – he was satisfied with the process.

He spent almost twenty minutes selecting his lunch, finally deciding on a ham and cheese sandwich on white
bread. The waitress smiled as she cut the crusts off for him.
He finished his sandwich slowly, keeping his eyes on the
busy streets outside. After lunch, he spent almost three
hours editing the last pages of the manuscript he was working on – a story set on a star. He loved the idea, and he'd finished most of the edit the day before; nevertheless, he ran
through it again, making tiny, last changes.

After that, he had finally run out of things to do.

Mr Dandelion got to his feet and slowly began to pack,
stacking books in boxes and double-checking every corner.

He thought about the day he'd first entered this office. He remembered the badly tailored suit he'd bought at a charity shop, and the blue tie he chose. How taken he was with the view. The first colleague he'd met was John, the man who'd taught him how to say no to proposals he didn't like – even though it remained his least favourite part of the job. John had left the company years ago. *He had a curious name*, Mr Dandelion thought, *Wooden? Woodborough? Woodland?* He pondered on this for a few minutes then sighed.

Now he had everything he'd ever kept in his office in two wooden boxes and he was sitting at his desk, his fingers tapping on its surface. There was nothing left to do but get up and go through his door for one last time and accept all the goodbyes and good lucks from his longtime colleagues. His walking stick stood in the doorway, as if to offer a helping hand on his departure – he'd had it for longer than he could recall, and the rubber grip on the bottom was once again in need of replacement.

There was a knock on the door and Eddie, the young and eager receptionist, stepped into his office.

'Are you ready, sir?'

'Ready for what, exactly?' Mr Dandelion raised an eyebrow.

'Your car. It's here.' Eddie smiled wide.

'They want me out of here so bad they even paid for a car...' he murmured. He tried to insist he would take the bus, but no, said Eddie, Russell, the editor-in-chief, would not hear of it.

Mr Dandelion reached for his boxes but Eddie had been quicker – he already stood in the doorway holding them, reminding Mr Dandelion of a puppy. He sighed again and without looking around, stepped out of his office and slowly walked down the hallway, smiling shyly and waving into every other office, his arm bent.

When Mr Dandelion finally had his things safely stored in his small apartment, and had waved away any further help that Eddie tried to offer him, he sat down at his dining table. He listened to the noises outside his window – he'd always heard the cars and buses passing by, but now he listened carefully as if for the first time. He had a cup of coffee in front of him, the instant kind that he made with just hot water and no sugar or milk, and he waited for it to cool as the minutes went by. He wasn't sure what to think about. For as many years as he could remember, he had spent his afternoons at the office – editing manuscripts or attending meetings, or readings, or launches – and the evening thinking about the things he'd done and the things he had to do the next day.

Now there was none of that.

The silence in his head felt deafening. He was sitting at his table with his coffee, like always, but could not find anything to think about. He knew that he couldn't delay *this* anymore – *this* had to come and he hadn't expected it to be pleasant. Even so, he couldn't decide why he felt the way he did. For most people, retirement was some kind of a reward for the years they'd spent working hard.

Mr Dandelion thought of it as a hole punched into his life.

He suddenly felt very alone.

It got darker outside. He flicked on the weak light in his living room and settled into his chair with an old edition of *The Sound and the Fury*, but he couldn't focus on the story, despite how many times he'd read it. His feet and hands felt weak. He was condemned to spend the rest of his days sitting in the same chair, he thought, until the day he quietly fell asleep. He imagined the situation – saw someone from the building eventually finding him, maybe because of the smell, maybe because of unpaid bills...

He scratched his head and decided that thinking about

his own death was not going to help him lighten up or get along. He looked at the clock. When he saw it showed 9.25pm, he decided this was an acceptable time to go to bed, even though he didn't feel tired. He flicked off the light in the living room and found the way to his bed in the dark.

On the day of his retirement, Roger Dandelion was 63, and even though he looked a little older to most, people said that he was well presented. He was short and very thin and his eyes seemed almost unnaturally blue. His hair had turned white a few years back, and now the top of his head was bald, with just a thin layer of hair on the sides. He almost always seemed to be uncertain about something – whether to smile or cry, whether to cross or wait for a green light, whether to buy the big can of beans that was more cost effective, or the small can that he actually preferred. He was a pleasant man to be around and a pleasant man to feel sorry for. He didn't speak much, and when he did, he always did so in the kindest manner. People liked Roger Dandelion, and Roger Dandelion tried hard to like them too.

When he was younger, Roger was very different. He was a handsome young man who seemed to glow with energy – he was full of ambitions and hopes, and when he met his wife, Julie, at the age of 24, he felt his life fulfilled. They were married before Roger turned 27.

On the day that Julie came home with a box of chocolates for Roger (his favourite type with dates and peanuts) and a piece of paper that declared she had an aggressive and rare breast cancer, he took a plate out of their cupboard and flung it to the floor, breaking it into a hundred little pieces – it was the angriest thing he had ever done, and he felt even angrier afterwards, angry at himself.

When Julie finally died, the only words he could muster at her funeral were 'I just can't believe it'.

Then he slowly turned old.

Whether Mr Dandelion ever considered remarrying, no one knew. He seemed to lock himself away in his tiny apartment when he wasn't in his office, and as everyone moved along in life, it seemed that he had been left behind in time. While everyone was occupied with mobile phones and tablets, he sat at his desk in his little office, edited hard copy manuscripts and spent the rest of his day admiring the view.

He woke up the next day with slight stomach pains. He pushed himself up on his elbows and turned his head from left to right, scanning the room. He saw nothing out of the ordinary. A single sock was hanging out of his top drawer; his old suitcase peeked out from behind the cupboard; his bedroom door was ever so slightly open and his curtains tightly shut, still letting through the spring sunshine. He tried to remember the details of his dream, sure that he'd had one, but couldn't: not faces, not actions, not sounds. All he had was a strange and familiar feeling, as if the unknown dream was true, nevertheless. He felt as if he might reach out and pull it back: immerse himself in it again.

He shook his head and got out of bed, sliding his feet into his slippers, putting on his copper-coloured, thinly framed glasses, then shuffled to the kitchen. It was a small, tight room with cupboards on two sides and a single narrow corridor. Facing the kitchen door was a window that overlooked a busy Notting Hill Gate tube station. He gazed out.

Everyone seemed to be in a hurry. Hundreds of people were rushing into and out of the station entrance. Shop doors were opening and closing; the clicking of heels and car horns echoed within the tight circle of buildings. Mr Dandelion watched one man until he disappeared around the corner of the street; then a woman, about 40, until she disappeared into the tube station.

He drummed a few notes on the windowsill and decided to get dressed. In his bedroom he chose an old beige shirt with black squares, and a pair of beige trousers.

Every morning he tried to slam the door shut with as much force as he could muster, and every morning, he had to try at least twice. There was some kind of problem with the locks, but Mr Dandelion had never felt the need to tell anyone. As long as he had enough force in his arms to shut it, he thought, he wouldn't get it fixed. So he slammed the door as he left – in the usual way, after checking his keys – and walked down the stairs, one step at a time, until he reached the spring day outside.

The area felt unexpectedly new; he saw all the coffee shops he could walk into, and he saw all the newsagents and bookshops and restaurants that were inviting him in, and he smiled a little. With his walking stick in one hand, taking every step slowly, he started down the high street, carefully looking into every window and reading every sign.

It was strange for him to be out on the street, instead of staring out the window of the bus that took him to work. But today, he thought, he was more than a man of habit – he was starting a new chapter of an unknown life.

The sun was hidden behind a thin layer of clouds – he could smell the rain that had fallen the night before – but he wasn't cold in his shirt. People passed him, rushing from one place to another, and in the midst of this hurry, he had the strange feeling he'd forgotten something; as if he was the only one not going anywhere. He passed a bookstore he liked, but didn't go in. *There's more to life than bookshops, Roger,* he thought, smiling resignedly, trying to remember the voice of his father. Then the idea seemed strange; his father would never have said such a thing. In fact, Dandelion Sr. would have spent his entire life in a bookshop. Mr Dandelion tried to picture his father the way he remembered him – he had a peculiar way of walking, his feet stepping a little to the side as he advanced, his back a little bent. Mr

Dandelion had been very close to his father, who always had a book for him to read, or a new idea if he felt a little lost.

He kept up his pace and walked on.

On the next corner, he noticed a shop he'd not seen before. It didn't seem that different from other bakeries and cafés in the area, apart from the fact that he'd never noticed the red and gold banners, or the windows so full of freshly baked goods that it was like a cloud of sweet fog. He was startled. This was the kind of thing he was looking for – something new – but now that he'd found it, he felt unsure. He peeked through the glass. Being a Friday, not many tables were occupied, and even then, mainly by elderly people sipping coffee and reading the papers. Mr Dandelion could picture himself inside, sitting at one of the little tables. He shifted his weight from one leg to the other and looked at the counter. A young woman in a red and gold apron was busy working the espresso machine. Her hair was tied up in a bouncy ponytail, and her hands were moving fast from machine to mug, from mug to milk.

He shook his head. *It's too empty.* He turned around and walked up on the high street towards home. On the way, he stopped by the bookshop and picked up a relatively new-looking copy of *Kafka: A Collection of Critical Essays*; he paid, keeping his eyes down on the book, then wandered home, the white plastic bag dangling in his hand.

As he shut the door behind him, he sighed. Suddenly the apartment seemed like the last place where he wanted to be: he felt sick of the walls, sick of the furniture, sick of the feeling that his home gave to him. He felt so tired of being where he was, and even more when he thought about the days to come that he would spend here. He wished he had somewhere to be, anywhere but there. He had failed today, and it left him feeling disappointed. He sat down in the living room, facing the window, and looked out on the street in silence.

Mr Dandelion awoke from an afternoon nap to his telephone ringing. As he sat up on his bed, it took him a few moments to realise where he was and why he was there. The phone rang. It seemed an alien sound, echoing in the corridor. He slid into his slippers and shuffled to the kitchen.

'Hello?'

'Roger? It's Kitty.'

Kitty Johnson was one of the few colleagues Mr Dandelion had regular contact with. Sometimes they even went on their lunch breaks together; he enjoyed Kitty's company, but by silent and mutual agreement they never saw each other outside of work. So Mr Dandelion was startled to hear the familiar voice on the phone for the first time.

She was a rather large woman with arms thicker than Mr Dandelion's thighs, and together they made the most unusual pair. She was respected by her colleagues, mostly because of her down to earth nature and her occasionally inappropriate jokes, and she liked to make loud comments about people she despised, always getting a shy smile from Mr Dandelion. Kitty was fearless, and he admired her for it.

'How are you doing?' she asked.

'Kitty... What can I help you with?'

'Well, you could answer my question for a start.' There was no smile in her voice. He stayed silent, checking for dirt under his nails.

'No need to be offended now, I was just wondering how retirement is treating you,' Kitty said, when no answer came.

'It's good... Thanks. It's treating me just fine. Lots of time and all that. I'm quite busy,' he murmured.

'Oh, good, good. Lots of time to do all the things you just couldn't do before.'

'Hah. Yes. Exactly.' He looked out the kitchen window.

'I completely forgot that you'd retired. I even went to your office to ask if you wanted a coffee.'

'That's kind of you.'

'I'd say it was rather stupid, but what the hell,' she laughed. 'Anyway, listen. Russell is looking for a project as-sistant next month. He's got some kind of manuscript com-ing in soon, and he's too lazy to go at it alone, apparently it's huge. You interested?'

'They want me back already?'

'They miss you like hell.'

'I'll think about it.'

'Fine. Just don't forget while you're at it,' she said.

'At it?'

'Whatever it is that keeps you busy,' she said with a little laugh. 'Not like I know. Have a nice day, Roger.'

'Same to you. Bye Kitty.'

He put the phone back and sat down to his dining table. *Working on a one-off, demanding manuscript could be good*, he thought, swirling the word 'demanding' around in his mouth, as if to taste it. He tried to convince himself, but it didn't feel right. Were they just trying to make him feel bet-ter? Had Russell ever hired an assistant before? He couldn't recall. Russell was a stubborn man, and an excellent editor. The idea seemed weird to him.

He looked at his watch – it was almost seven and the sky was getting dark outside. He walked to the kitchen and after a bit of looking around, took a can of chicken korma out of the cupboard. He emptied it into an old pan while he hummed a tune under his breath; to anyone observing, he might have even seemed jolly. He took a slice of bread from the cupboard to compliment the canned dinner, and toasted it. He ate his dinner quietly at his table as he watched the street lights come on. Friday night: his day was coming to an end, but the traffic thickened. He felt worse than he had yes-terday; so much that he had forgotten about the book he'd bought earlier. The thought cheered him up a little. After finishing his meal, he settled in his living room and read several of the Kafka essays. When his thoughts wandered so badly he couldn't remember what he'd read on the last few pages, he got into bed. He looked around his room again; all was quiet. He turned off his reading lamp, closed his eyes and rolled onto his side, away from the window.

BLANK

Karoline Vembre

1

Look through me and you see pale ice drifting on the freez-
ing water. You see rocks, cold on the snow-covered beaches.
You see blue from the depths of the water rise and touch the
sky. The sun sets at three and the ice turns to rain in my
palms. You see the silent road. The grey pebbles. The house.
You hear the silence, in the creaking door. You see it in the
windows, the white paint peeling off the walls. Look
through me and you see the wind, shifting on naked
branches. Ice drifting with the tide, indecisive, unreliable.
See through me and there is silence.

2

I kissed the tip of his finger, looked at him. He smiled.
　　Tell me, he said.
　　What?
　　I want to know.
　　For what?
　　I want to know you.
　　His knuckles were bruised. Red. I leaned back against
the wall. He laid his head on the bed. The sheets were com-
ing off.
　　How long have you been here?
　　A while.
　　I grew up here, in the city. Where did you grow up?

The inch gap between the dusty curtains showed the dark sky outside. The white T-shirt he'd given me had a black ink stain on one of the sleeves. I licked my finger and rubbed it against the stain.

We moved around. He turned and looked up at the ceiling. The traffic outside made the walls shiver. I touched his ankle with my toes and watched his eyes trace the cracks in the ceiling.

Do you want to know me?

I don't know. Are you interesting? I said.

He sat up. Lit two cigarettes and gave one to me. The floor was scattered with butts.

You should get an ashtray.

I'm quitting.

Yeah.

Have been for a while.

We exhaled. The smoke between us collided.

I'm not.

Ever?

When it kills me. I'll stop when it kills me.

He smiled. The lamplight carved his shadow out into the wall behind him. It hung on a string from the ceiling, swaying. His shadow wavered. The wallpaper was peeling off.

He laid his hand on my knee. Then we should, he said.

What?

Get an ashtray.

For me?

Both of us. You'll be around for a while?

For a while.

I leaned out of the bed and stubbed my cigarette out on the spotted wooden floor.

3

The house was steady and stood like the rocks, unchanged

for as long as I lived. The paint on the white walls peeled, but never let go. The house was at the end of the road. Furthest from the bridge, closest to the open sea. My father's mother and her father, and probably his father too, had lived here. Their framed faces lined the walls. Grave and colourless, their dead eyes watched over us.

I talked to them when I was younger. I remember it well. I talked to the woman with the pearl necklace, the man with the black eyes, the girl with the sharp bones, the boy with the knee-high socks. He was my favourite, the boy. I called him Olav, because there was an O in the corner of the frame. I remember telling him stories. I told him I'd found a white bunny rabbit in the garden, I told him I'd climbed the rocks by the waterfall, I told him I'd seen a submarine by the beach.

4

They all smelled like burnt paper, like fire and blackened ash. Their lips were stained purple from red wine and sore from kissing. It was the first week in the city. I drank something transparent, sat in a black leather chair. My jeans were ripped above the knee.

Where are you from? people said.

You wouldn't know it.

So what are you doing here?

Not sure.

A boy sat down on the table in front of me. He was freckled and had crooked teeth. You don't look like you're having much fun.

I guess I'm not.

He put his hand on my knee. He had skinny wrists.

And why is that?

I crossed my legs, looked in his eyes. My brother died.

Oh no.

Yeah. My dad shot him.

The boy looked at me. Raised his eyebrows.

Your dad shot him?

Yeah. They were hunting.

Really?

Yeah, he thought my brother was a deer. Cried out in celebration as he shot him. First deer of the year. That's what he thought. I sipped my drink.

The boy took his hand off my knee.

Oh.

Buy me a drink?

The boy nodded and walked to the bar. I emptied my glass and got up. The entrance was crowded, but I pushed my way out. I didn't want another drink.

5

My father asked me again, and I told him again. I made him coffee, no sugar, no milk. He smiled his childlike smile and looked out the window. He could tell time by watching the water, how high the waves hit the rocks. I could tell time by watching his eyes, the bewilderment returning as the hours passed. He would ask me again, and I would tell him again. We both knew time was not passing, not taking us forwards, but continuous and reoccurring. He had trouble sleeping the last few months. He would wake up in the middle of the night mumbling, moving around. I never asked him what he was dreaming of. Afraid I might dream it too.

6

It was the third night I'd slept in his flat. The crack in the ceiling began to look familiar. I knew where to step to avoid the cigarettes on the floor. He put on music when he got out of bed. Sang to the records as he made coffee.

Milk? Sugar?

None.

Black it is.

We drank the coffee on the windowsill. Watched the grey smoke from the chimneys blend with the pale yellow dusk. Watched the birds' black silhouettes against the city fog. He lived on the fifth floor. The staircase smelled like cat piss, but the view was nice. We watched the cars pass on the street below.

Are you going to show me your place anytime soon?

Wasn't planning on it.

No?

What for? It's a dump.

I don't care.

I like it better here, anyway.

He smiled. He had a small coffee moustache at the edges of his mouth.

Stay as long as you want.

Thanks.

He put on more coffee, rolled a cigarette on the kitchen counter. We could hear voices yelling though the walls. A woman shouted.

You have nowhere you have to be? He looked at me. Someone punched the wall. There was more shouting.

No. Nowhere.

Nothing you have to do?

No. Not right now.

A door slammed. No job?

We looked at each other. No.

He smiled. So where does the money come from?

Someone threw something across the room next door. We heard glass breaking. Loud swearing.

You tell me.

I snatched the cigarette out of his hand. He watched me smoking.

No money?

Don't worry. I'm figuring it all out.

The neighbours' door slammed shut again. The windows shook. Someone ran down the stairs.

Those people are crazy, I said.

He smiled. We looked at each other. Tell me about it.

7

I walked half an hour to school every day. Back and forth down the pebbled road. There were abandoned houses scattered along the seaside, roofs fallen in and windows broken. Most of the other children lived on the other side of the island. In the winter, I walked with a flashlight hung around my neck. The streetlights were unreliable.

I always imagined people walking around the abandoned houses. Imagined children running on the overgrown lawns. I made up names for them. Imagined there were boys in all the houses. One of them played the piano, another carved birds out of wood. The boys would run out, when they saw me pass. They would open their battered front doors and call my name. They would walk me home. Fighting to hold my hand. I would tell them to stop, to go home. But they kept walking with me, circling me, telling me stories and asking me to kiss them. I never let them into my house, always left them by the gate. I used to lock the door when I got in. Look through the window and see them, all standing there by the fence, watching me, watching the house.

8

I got a job in a bar, after a month. It was dark with dusty lampshades and old wooden tables. The people who came there were mostly old drunks. They would moan about their lives, tell each other things always got better, hug and buy each other drinks. I mixed their vodka with water and drank in the storage room. All the bartenders were long-legged, skinny girls. The boss was a creep.

Sweetie, get me another, will you?

No problem.

Say, what is a girl like you doing working here?

The old man had a deep voice. Sore with whisky.

What do you mean?

Why aren't you in school?

Oh well, you know.

He leaned across the counter, his unshaved face moist with spilled wine.

What?

They kicked me out.

Really?

He came closer, his hand tight around his glass.

Yeah. Stabbed a teacher with some scissors.

What?

Yeah. They didn't like that.

The old man looked at me. He opened his mouth, but said nothing.

It wasn't even deep, I said.

I cleaned a glass against the sleeve of my shirt. The old man turned on his stool and staggered towards a booth in the corner. He whispered something to his friends. I smiled at them.

9

My father told me he had chosen my name. That I was named after a song he had loved. He told me again, over and over and every time I asked him what song. He waited; searching the fragments of his memory, and then shook his head. The snow melted off the hillsides. Made small streams that ran beside our house. We could hear them inside. The water rippling against the rocks. My father watched the hill-sides through the window. Watched and waited for the snow to melt. He asked me what had happened. He asked me what had happened again. I told him. I told him again. He asked me. He asked me again. I told him. I told him again. He asked me, and then, I told him something different. I told him something different every time.

10

His breathing filled the room. The slow motion of his chest and the repetition of his breath. I watched the ceiling. The crack was widening. Stretching towards the wall. I couldn't sleep. I couldn't sleep, waiting for the crack in the ceiling to reach the wall.

Are you awake?

Couldn't sleep.

Why not?

Not sure.

He turned and looked at me. His eyes were tired, dry with sleep. What's on your mind?

Too much.

He sat up. Tell me.

I thought about what I might say. What thoughts I might have. He looked at me.

It's just too quiet.

He nodded and sat up. Started walking around the room, looking for something. I watched the crack in the ceiling. Wondered what was above us. What was pressing down on us.

It's rare. That it's quiet.

Mhm.

But you don't like it.

I wondered when the ceiling would cave in. I shook my head. He stood next to the stereo. Flicked through his records.

Strange. I find myself looking for it.

What?

The quiet.

He found the right record and placed it on the stereo. This is a great record. A song started playing. It always helps me sleep.

He got back into bed. The song was quiet, slow. A man sang about the rain and the city streets. He pulled me closer to him. I fell asleep.

11

When my father woke up he didn't recognise himself. He couldn't understand who he was or who we were. He sat in his hospital bed staring at the clock on the wall. He asked me what it was. I told him a clock, a clock that measures time. He stared at it. Asked me again. I told him again. He asked me again. I told him a clock, it's used to measure time.

12

I sat on the stairs outside my apartment finishing a cigarette. It was February. The streets were quiet. Clouds faded in the sky and sunlight broke through: glistening in the puddles, reflecting in windows. Last night's rainwater dripped from the gutter.

You're on fourth, right? A girl stood at the foot of the stairs. She held a cat in her hands. It seemed to be sleeping. The girl smiled at me. She had a black T-shirt on and white hair pulled up into a knot. A birthmark stretched from her left temple towards her eye.

Yeah. I nodded. Stubbed out the cigarette. And you?

Loft. With my Gran.

The girl stroked the cat. It did not move. I found this cat.

You see.

I got up, leaning on the rusting railing. I looked down at her.

It's dead, I said.

The girl stroked her fingers over its unmoving chest. A car passed on the street behind her: the pulsing of its bass filling the air for a moment.

I found it in the playground behind the estate.

I walked down the steps to where the girl stood. The cat was small, pale brown. Its eyes were closed; one of them had a scratch right across it. The fur was wet and smeared with mud.

What are you going to do with it? I reached for another cigarette.

I don't know. I've never found something dead before.

I lit the cigarette. More cars passed on the road behind us, casting water up into the air.

You should bury it.

The girl nodded and kept stroking the cat. Yeah. Maybe. She hesitated. It's not illegal is it? Burying a cat that you find in a ditch.

Not at all.

The girl smiled. She had dimples. You want to come? She looked at me, tilting her head, hugging the cat.

Why not?

Thanks. It wouldn't be much fun having the funeral on my own.

She started walking down the road, humming a song. I followed, spinning my keys around my fingers.

We'll go to the brick wall, she called over her shoulder. That's a nice place to be dead.

We crossed the river behind the estate and continued up the concrete road.

The girl had dug the grave out with her hands. Water

reached the edges and fell into the black earth. I had taken some flowers from a vase taped to a cross outside a church we'd passed. White lilies.

All things deserve to be buried.

The girl lowered the cat into the hole. The flowers lay by her feet.

I wouldn't want to be left in a ditch by the playground.

She sat down in the dirt and stroked the cat. The wet mud stained her jeans.

You think it was killed? I think it was killed.

She patted the nose, stroked the whiskers so that they lay down straight.

It looks cold down there.

She stroked the ear so that it moved backwards and forwards. I sat down next to her.

The cat's not cold. It's dead.

The girl nodded.

Right.

She pushed the wet dirt into the hole, closing it off, burying the cat. Then she laid the flowers on top. Their white buds spotted with mud. She kept one flower in her hand.

At least the flowers were blessed.

She looked at the grave. Rolled the lily around between her fingers.

I haven't been to a funeral since I was a baby.

The girl patted the dirt on top of the grave, her handprint appearing in the mud.

What happens after? She looked at me.

Then there is the repast.

Repast?

I brushed the dirt off my legs. Let's go have some beers.

Right.

The girl laughed. I helped her to her feet.

I'm Sandy, by the way.

Sandy put a white lily behind her ear.

13

My father knew every country in the world, but had never left our island. The traces of his life were everywhere in our house. His height as a boy, carved into my bedroom door. His pencil drawings on the old nightstand. His footprints were immortalized in the cement floor of the shed. His first girlfriend's initials framed by a heart on a tree in our garden The poems he scribbled in the margins of books still clear against the paper. The number of his best friend as a child still noted in crooked writing on the back of the old receiver. His handprint on the ceiling, drawn as he lay on his back in the top bunk still steady, still clear against the wooden panel. I had measured my fingers against it as a child. In the night when I could not sleep I placed my hand on his hand and found relief in the way they fitted together. My father was everywhere, but he couldn't see it. He would walk around in the rooms he grew up in, wondering whose house he was in.

LIKE MARIGOLDS
Emily Parsons

Then our car hit the tree.

And I stumbled into the night. And there was the cloud and the darkness that stood over me. Trembling. Ready to spill water. Ready to strike my back with lightning. I crouched, rocked, knees round my ears. I watched lights zip through the cloud, felt the ground sliding away beneath my fingers. My shoulders stiffened.

The cloud rolled forward. I breathed it in. It tasted like water from the mountains. Like snow from the peak. I swallowed it.

Then the cloud swallowed me.

I don't remember much before that. Only shouts and murmurs. Fern's laugh and 'you little shit'. A sleeping horse and a red-eyed possum that scuttled in front of us. The hum of tyres on ice, and screams.

I left the hospital eighteen hours later with stitches over my left eyebrow and a big bottom lip where my teeth had pushed through. Fern was wailing. Pulling at his eyelashes and calling for Mum. I left those white walls with Aunty Mae propping up my head on her hip, her arm round my shoulders and Fern clinging to her, making her two-day-unwashed shirt wet.

Mum left in a wooden box that we pushed into a fire. It ate her up and left us with a box of sand. I would never go to the beach again.

When we threw her over the edge of Devil's Gullet, the

winds brought a bit of her back into our faces. She coated my lips and stung my eyes. That night at tea, all I could taste was Mum.

She always loved Devil's Gullet. Called it the Grand Canyon of Tasmania. She'd take us there whenever she could. Had this trick where she'd throw my hat over the edge. The wind would catch it and send it flying into the bushes behind us. I caught it on my head, once. Got a round of cheers from camera-faced tourists and a bag of chocolate freckles from Mum. Maybe that was why she had us put her there. One last trick.

After the wattle box was empty, we sat and watched her float down the cliff face and out over the mountains. Aunty Mae, Uncle Alec, Fern and me, just watching dust over trees. Aunty Mae had big tears that clung to her eyelashes. I wondered if she'd gotten sand in her eyes too. Aunty Mae was Mum's twin. Identical. Imagine watching your twin slipping around in the wind.

The longer I looked at her, eyes flicking back and forth trying to hold onto a speck of Mum, the sicker I felt. Not in my stomach, more in my lungs, this slow rattle. Aunty Mae and Mum always looked most alike when they cried. I couldn't help watching her. It was like watching Mum.

Fern sucked on the metal railing that stopped us from falling off the edge of the mountain. Or jumping. I watched him staring into the valley. We were orphans. Like in the books. I'd never known anyone in real life to be an orphan. I looked up at the adults, said, 'Aunty Mae, are we orphans now?' She looked down at me and started bawling out loud. She dropped beside me. Buried my face in the canyon between her boobs.

'Oh, Tilly. No. No. No!' That was all she said. We stayed like that until the sky went red and made our shadows as long as giants. Uncle Alec picked up Aunty Mae and dragged her down the path to the car. Gave me a nod and I did the same with Fern.

Mum was dead. Dad was long gone. It was just us.

The car ride home was quiet. The only sounds were Fern crying and Aunty Mae's wedding ring tapping on the window, where she cupped her cheek.

We drove through a tunnel of trees that stopped suddenly; we moved into unsheltered paddocks. As we drove into the shadow of the mountains, it got hard to breathe deep and proper. I wasn't sure if it was the smell of all the donated casseroles in the back, or the way Uncle Alec's eyes kept flicking between me and the road, in the rear-view mirror. He had this look. A mix of pity and disgust. It reminded me of Ashley Green in primary school. She hated me. I hated her. She had that exact look when I got hit in the face with a netball during P.E. I had to lie on the court, pinching my nose, looking up at her laughing. It took everything I had not to kick her.

That look, the childishness of it, made me so mad. I knew he didn't want me there. Reminded him too much of Mum, I reckon. They were friends when they were young, but then something in him changed and he wouldn't talk to her. Made me wonder how he could stand being with Aunty Mae. Maybe that was why she dyed her hair brown, kept it sleek and straight cut, while Mum's was long and blonde and tangled. Why she wore makeup while Mum was clean-faced. And why she kept her skin like canvas while Mum was brown and spotted.

I should've told him off. Told him to keep his eyes on the road. But I didn't. Didn't want to wake Fern and Aunty Mae. Or maybe I was just gutless. So I sat there, silent, feeling like I could puke at any second.

When we got to the house, I sat in the car for a minute, too tired to move. I watched the sun finally set as everyone else stumbled inside. I watched the mountain's shadow eat the little white cottage and the lamps inside, popping on until each flaking weatherboard was lit up.

It's just a house, I told myself. You've been here before. You've lived here before. You've been back to visit. Nothing's changed.

But I was wrong.

I stepped inside. The air felt cold and so strange. I don't know how to describe it. Don't have the words. It was like Mum wasn't the only thing we left up at Devil's Gullet. It was like that feeling you get when you see a painting that's too good. Too life-like. It makes you pull into yourself. Your chest presses down and your shoulders come up round your jaw. There's something not right, but you can't quite get at it.

I'd spent the first seven years of my life in that house. My father's house. Always warm. The cream walls glowing from the fire and the carpet like moss. Every corner freckled with the spit from our laughter. Then he left. We swapped houses with Aunty Mae and Uncle Alec and the house began to cool. I guess that's what happens when kids leave a place and just-adults take over. Everything becomes too clean. No mossy carpet. No spit freckled walls. No greasy palm prints on glass doors. Just a house.

I stood in the kitchen while Aunty Mae and Uncle Alec wove around me, putting away casseroles and 'Sorry For Your Loss' cards. I counted squares of lino to make sure there was still as many as I remembered.

'Come on, Til. I can't do all the heavy lifting. Need your muscles,' Uncle Alec said. Then he smiled. I knew he was putting it on for Aunty Mae, but what a day to smile. Mum was still floating around over the mountains, hadn't even settled, and he was smiling.

I looked at him. Didn't say a word. His lip twitched, ready to pull the whole structure down. He coughed and looked away. I breathed out and went to the car to get my bag. By the time I got back inside he was gone. To check the cows, Aunty Mae said, but I didn't believe it.

I slid my things up the long dark hall to my new room. My old room. My new-old room. The hall, decorated with those same old photos from when I was little. The photograph of the farm from above. The grainy black and white shots of sweaty men standing next to logs as wide as they were tall. They looked so happy, standing next to those giant logs, long-saw propping up their tired arms.

For a second I felt sad that no one would get to see a tree that wide and long because they'd all been chopped to make houses. I wondered how many trees it took to make this cold-aired cottage.

I paused outside my new-old bedroom door. White with dark green trim and a plaque that said 'Wattle Pearce'. Hand painted with little yellow splotches around it. Next to it, one that said 'Fern Pearce' with dark green fronds under it. I ran my fingers over the lumpy paint. Still gluey. Probably Aunty Mae's way of making us feel wanted.

Wattle Pearce, what a name. Always misspelled, always questioned. There was this look that every new teacher got when they read it from the register. Like one of us kids had gotten into something and was playing a trick on them. Most would just go for my middle name, Maria. When I'd tell them it was Wattle-but-call-me-Tilly, they'd just shake their heads. Heard one of them say 'bloody hippy parents' under their breath when I was eight. Told Mum. She wasn't too pleased. Never saw *that* relief teacher again.

Dad named me, after the tree. Said he was watching me in the hospital, all brown and long with this puff of yellow hair, and it just came to him. Mum was too knackered to stay awake. Dad decided to grab the birth certificate and fill it out for her as a surprise. 'She'd already done so much, thought it was my turn,' he'd say. So I was named 'Wattle

Maria (after Mum) Pearce'.

Mum had a fit when she woke up and found out what he'd done. She wouldn't stop crying, or spluttering 'But... we... can't... call... her... that! I wanted to call her Matilda. We're not fucking hippies!' Dad always loved to include that bit. He never censored real conversations, not even to four-year-olds. He said she looked like she was in more pain than when she was giving birth.

In the end they compromised, called me Tilly. People could decide it was short for whatever they wanted, Matilda or Wattle. Seven years later and my brother was born. By then Mum had come around to the idea of plant names, so they called him Fern.

I walked into my new-old room. It looked the same as the last night I'd spent in it. The night he left. The walls, powder blue with streaks of white from Mum's shoddy paint job. My bed, old timber that smelled like the forest and gave you splinters if you ran your finger over it. Dad made it. Didn't want to oil it, said it ruined the smell. That smell of wet bark and bundled mushrooms. I pressed my nose to the wood. I could just get it. The smell of the bush. The smell of home.

In the corner was Fern's new bed. Next to it, dismantled and leaning against the wall, his old cot. A gift from Mum to Aunty Mae. She'd never used it. I would've liked a cousin, but I guess Aunty Mae and Uncle Alec weren't into having kids. What was it going to be like, being raised by two people who didn't even like kids enough to have their own?

I asked Aunty Mae why they never had any later at dinner. She pushed lasagne around her plate, cleared her throat, said, 'Oh, I guess we've just never had time. Really.' She looked tired. Uncle Alec's knuckles were white around his fork, but he didn't say anything.

'Yes,' she said, 'just not enough time.'

Fern's eyes went wide.

'But, you'll have time for us?' he said through a mouthful of mince.

'Yes, dear. Yes, of course we'll have time for you. All the time in the world.' She wiped sauce from Fern's chin and smiled. I couldn't tell if she meant it. I was distracted by the sand in my teeth. She sighed. Uncle Alec reached for more garlic bread. I didn't bring up kids with them again.

The night dragged on. Fern sat twitching in his chair, shifting from cheek to cheek, like he needed to wee. He kept glancing at Aunty Mae and Uncle Alec, licking his lips to say something, then stopping himself. They didn't notice. They were counting down the minutes until they could send us to bed. Maybe it was good they didn't have any kids. They had no clue what to do with us. At eight-thirty Uncle Alec cracked his toes and declared it was time for bed.

We went without protest. Every part of me was tired. We brushed, washed, combed and slid into Mum's old t-shirts that were soft and smelled like the tea-tree oil she'd rub on her cheeks to clear her skin.

Aunty Mae came in, sat on Fern's bed to say goodnight. Uncle Alec stood in the doorway, picking at paint.

'It's been a long day, huh?' Aunty Mae said and tucked some of Fern's woolly hair behind his ear. He smiled. She looked around, as if unsure of what to say next.

'Yeah,' I said, not quite sure either. Then I yawned to confirm it. She seemed to appreciate that.

'Well, we'll let you get some rest. Just give us a call if you need anything. Anything at all.' She kissed Fern's head. He looked ready to burst. She got up to leave, 'Night, Fern.'

'Night, Mum,' Fern said, loud and quick, like a sneeze.

Aunty Mae stopped, her eyes frozen on Uncle Alec, her throat all tense and lips trembling. I looked at Uncle Alec. He was standing completely still. Upright. Not even breathing. But I could see his teeth grinding away beneath black stubble. They breathed out together.

'No,' she said. Cleared her throat, turned to Fern. 'No, dear. Not Mum. Don't call me that. I, I will love you like a mother, but, don't call me that.'

'What do we call you then?' Fern asked. His voice was barely heard from behind the blankets he was pulling over his face. My lungs started that rattle again and I had to claw my toes into the sheets to stop myself from grabbing him and running. I wanted to speak, back Fern up with some-thing, but the only words I could think of were gibberish swearwords.

Aunty Mae looked at Uncle Alec. He shrugged. She looked at me. I shook my head and pulled my knees to my chest.

Fern's small voice splintered the silence. 'It's just, it's just that 'Aunty Mae' and 'Uncle Alec' is harder to say in emer-gencies than 'Mum' or 'Dad'.'

'What do you mean?' she asked. I could see the relief soak through her. Uncle Alec stayed stiff in the doorway.

Fern pulled the blankets down from his face. His cheeks were all pink. 'If Tilly was bashing me up, and I wanted to call for help, youse can hear 'Mum!' better than youse can hear 'Aunty Mae!' That's all.'

I unpicked my toes from the sheets. Flexed them. I smiled into my blankets and looked at Fern. That kid, I swear. Mind like a philosopher. He looked around, scrunching up his lip like he'd cry if I didn't say something soon.

'He's right,' I said. His lip unscrunched. 'All good names need to be easy to yell. One syllable, done. It's the first thing you learn when you get a dog.'

'What would you suggest then Til?' Aunty Mae smiled and slid onto Fern's bed again.

'Umm...'

'No, um'll be too confusing.' She laughed. I pulled a face at her. She had the same sense of humour as Mum. I liked that. Uncle Alec just kept grinding his teeth.

Aunty Mae drummed her fingers on her thighs. 'Why don't you just call us Mae and Alec? No Aunty and Uncle.'

'Well, they are easier to yell.' I shrugged. Fern yelled 'Mae', giggled and said, 'yep, it works.'

'Okay then.' She breathed out. First names would work.

'Hey Mae. Whaddaya say, it's nearly May, Mae!' Fern sang.

'Stop it, you.' She put her fingers on Fern's lips, smiled. 'Okay. Night you two.'

'Night Mae-May. Night Alec.' Fern shuffled down into his bed.

'Night Fern. Night Tilly.'

'Night Mae. Night Uncle Alec.' I said.

'Just Alec,' said Uncle Alec through his teeth. I was surprised he had any left.

'Yep.' I sunk under my covers, used them to cover my smile. There was a quiet joy in making him feel uncomfortable.

'Night then.' He tapped the doorframe and left. Mae smiled and blew us a kiss before she turned out the light.

I lay awake half the night, thinking to the sound of Fern's hiccups and the wind outside.

School was back from Easter, but Mae took us out. Said we didn't have to go back until we were ready. I was ready, but lied and said I didn't think I'd ever be ready. She hugged me, said 'I know'. Said we'd get through it together. I smiled, but I couldn't help thinking that I didn't want her or Uncle Alec to be part of my 'together'. I didn't want someone who looked like Mum or someone who hated me pretending to be my parents. I just wanted Fern. Me and the kid, getting through it together.

Everyone at the funeral said how grown up I looked, how mature, how strong. And that was fine, but I wanted to

be more, for Fern, for the two orphaned Pearce kids. Orphans in books tackled bigger problems than this all the
time, why not us?

We took to exploring the farm, me and Fern, with all our
free time. Walking through paddocks, whacking tall grass
with sticks, feeling like we could melt into the country air.

The day after we moved back into the new-old house,
we sat in the paddock by the front drive, watching clouds
and making up songs on a blade of grass. Uncle Alec's old
kelpie, Dusty, came running through the fence with seven
little pups close behind. They jumped at our faces, covered
us in slobber and scratches. Fern took off, running mad after
them, hiding behind tall grass and rolling in the dirt.

Dusty settled, panting behind my back, happy for the
break. One pup, the runt I guess, crawled onto my lap,
started sucking on my jeans. I ran my fingers over his fur;
warm and soft from the sun.

I looked at the house, settled beneath the mountains.
This white egg in a nest of golden wattle trees that wouldn't
blossom until spring. God, I'd forgotten how beautiful the
farm was. Especially later in the year, usually September,
when the wattles that bordered the house and forest
erupted in fluffy yellow flowers. We used to run out on
windy days to shake the branches and watch the blossoms
fly off like confetti in the wind.

The pup took advantage of my wandering mind, started
chewing on my fingers.

'Ouch! You little bastard.' I held the pup in front of my
face, nose to nose, and pouted at him. He barked and stuck
his tongue up my nostril. I laughed. Fern bounded up.

'What's so funny?' he asked, breathless.

'This little guy's just licked the inside of me nose.'

'Ewww. He ate your boogers?'

'Yep.'

'But...' he paused, looked around concerned. My chest

tightened. '...what are you gonna eat for afternoon tea now?' He looked at me, all serious for a second, then started laughing.

'Don't do that to me, you dick!' I threw a hunk of dirt at him.

'Better than being a booger eater.' He threw it back, hard. I chased him around the paddock. Caught him and tickled him till he screamed he was gonna wet himself.

We lay on the grass, Fern's head on my belly, my head on Dusty's back and the pups suckling on the other side.

'I'm glad you're not mean no more,' Fern said when his breath came back.

'I wasn't mean,' I said and poked a finger into his ribs.

'Yeah you was. What about that time you stuffed me under the couch and I couldn't breathe?'

'Hey. You farted in my face,' I laughed.

'I couldn't *breathe*!' he sat up, hovered over me, eyes all big in disbelief, like I'd done the worst thing ever.

'Yeah-but, that was only once.'

'What about when you got me stuck in the blocks bucket?' We had this big bucket of Duplo blocks. I figured it could fit someone in it, easy. When I was Fern's age I tried. Got stuck with my bum wedged in the bucket, arms and legs hanging over the edge with no way to get out. When Fern was big enough I got him to do the same. Sat there laughing and eating grapes while he tried to wiggle free. I helped him out after half an hour.

'Yeah okay. Maybe I was.'

'You were,' he flopped back down, head on my chest, bare feet tearing up grass.

I wrapped my arm around him. 'I'm glad I'm not mean anymore too.'

We lay there, watching clouds, until Mae called us in for lunch.

NOTES ON CONTRIBUTORS

All contributors are either winners of the annual Creative Writing Day anthology competition, organised by the Department of English and Creative Writing at the University of Roehampton, or their work has been chosen for publication by the programme's staff. Unless stated otherwise, they are current or former students of the university with the degree BA Honours with Creative Writing (single or combined) as an award subject. Where applicable, the year of graduation is indicated in brackets.

RUDOLF AMMANN, PhD, is a research associate at the UCL Department of Information Studies and chief artist at the Arkstack.co.uk design consultancy in London. He has created book covers and interior templates for Fincham Press and advised on production workflow since its inception.

ELISABETH B. ANDERSEN [2015] lives near Oslo, Norway, and is moderately obsessed with fairy tales. At the time of publication she is working on a short story collection and a novel, both untitled. Her short fiction is also published in the erotic fairytale anthology, *Lustily Ever After* by Two Dames Press (2016). Andersen wonders why everything she writes turns into magical realism, and is secretly waiting for her admissions letter to Hogwarts.

KATHERINE ARMSTRONG intends her writing style to resemble her personality: direct, thoughtful and provocative. She is not afraid to write openly about sexuality, bodily functions and mental illness, and likes to find beauty in the mundane or distasteful. Her influences range from Kafka and Burroughs to Hieronymus Bosch, and the toys and 1950s anthropomorphic vegetable jars she collects.

JESSE BEDAYN's father was a mountaineer, and instilled in him a love of the Sierra Nevada Mountains, which loom large in his writing. Bedayn enjoys the classics, modern philosophers, critics, poets, and novelists. He has studied philosophy, writing, and linguistics in London. *The Anemoi* is his first published work.

FATHIMA BEGUM [2016] is a fiction writer. Her story, *Patterns*, is a semi-autobiographical work. When not writing, she loves watching Bollywood films and adding more products to her already huge collection of make-up. This is her first submission to a competition.

NANOU BLAIR GOULD [2014] writes novels, short stories and plays. At the time of publication she is preparing *Poppycock* for the Camden Fringe and editing her novel *To Spite the Weevil*. She has satisfactorily convinced herself that red wine is the answer to writer's block. She doesn't really believe in writer's block.

CHARLOTTE BYRNE published her first short story, *Soldiers All*, in a bilingual anthology by DualBooks in 2013. She writes with dogs at her feet and tea to hand, or sometimes the other way around. Byrne is Fincham Press's first publishing intern. At time of publication she is pursuing her MA in Creative Writing at Roehampton University.

NIKA COBBETT [2015] is, at the time of publication, preparing herself to study at Oxford University for her Masters in Creative Writing. Her story, *The Small Things,* was born from a feeling that she couldn't control her characters. This is her second publication with Fincham Press.

BRAD COHEN is a poet whose writing explores the unexpected beauty in adversity, such as same-sex love and religion, reflected here in his first published poem, *Church.* At the time of publication, he is working on his first poetry collection/multi-media exhibition, in collaboration with an artist. Cohen's details and portfolio can be found on his website www.bradcohen.co.uk.

LLOYD COLE [2016] is from Essex. His poem, *A Cat,* details his daily journey home and is written in the style of Frank O'Hara, whose collection *Why I Am Not A Painter* particularly inspired him. He can be found on Twitter at @LloydCole258085.

JALICE CORRAL is a combined Creative Writing and Drama, Theatre and Performance Studies student from Baltimore. Her story *Ducks & Horses* is based on her father's frequent fibbing during her childhood. This is her first publication.

CHLO EDWARDS's series of haiku, *Singular,* is her first published work. She is also a musician, who before coming to Roehampton toured internationally with her band, Vales. The central theme of *Singularity* is finding beauty in moments of melancholy.

IDUNN ELVRUM [2016] won her year's Creative Writing Prize in 2015 and – despite stubbornly declaring she was not a poet – the Hopkins Poetry Prize in 2016 for *Endemic.* At the time of publication, she plans to teach English in Japan, although becoming a nomad would be preferable.

DUSTIN FRAZIER WOOD, PhD, is a specialist in early medieval literature and medievalism studies. He received his PhD from the University of St Andrews in 2013 and has since published on aspects of Old English literature and culture, early modern medieval studies, and antiquarianism. He has recently completed his first book, *Anglo-Saxonism and the Idea of Englishness, 1703-1805*. Frazier Wood is Renner Visiting Scholar in English at Bethany College in the United States, and a member of the editorial board for Fincham Press.

SUSAN L. GREENBERG, PhD, took up teaching and research after a long career as writer and editor for newspapers, magazines and the web. She is Senior Lecturer in the Department of English and Creative Writing at Roehampton, specialising in narrative nonfiction and publishing, and a founding member of the Fincham Press editorial board. Her latest book is *Editors talk about editing: insights for readers, writers and publishers* (Peter Lang, 2015).

KATHERINE GUTIERREZ [2016] is a writer of fiction and short stories, and has previously contributed to the *Screams and Silences* 2015 anthology by Fincham Press. Her titular story, *Purple Lights* won the editor's choice award at the 2015 Roehampton Creative Writing Day Competition soiree. In March 2016, her short story, *The Pilgrims*, was featured as The Weekend Read podcast at For Books' Sake, a website that promotes excellent literature written by women authors.

PATRICK HAWKES lives in London and has been unsuccessfully employed several times, most notably for a month at Sweatbox Soho, after which he was sacked. With literary influences that include Evelyn Waugh and Christopher Isherwood, Patrick enjoys long walks in the park, vintage champagne and 60s Brit rock.

Rob Heimann is a writer and observer of curiosities. At the time of publication, Rob was working selling high-end beer, wine and cheese. He hopes one day to find a way to say 'I'm a writer' without sounding pretentious.

Maria Highland [2015] studied for an MA in Historical Research since graduating from Roehampton. This is her first publication by Fincham Press. Her short story, *Not the One*, subverts the notion of romance through a 'daisy chain' of events, depicting the relationship failures of a self-protective protagonist.

Hannah Hodson [2015] lives in North Lincolnshire and writes poetry. The poems featured here were inspired by Gertrude Stein and replicate her innovative, unique form of writing. As a qualified fitness instructor and creative writer, Hannah finds the two combine to make the ideal outlet for expression. She can be found on Twitter at @hanactive.

Stiina-Sofia Honkavaara published her first creative work as a Roehampton undergraduate, in the *Roehampton Writes* web magazine (2013). At the time of publication, she is finishing an MA in Creative Writing at Roehampton. She loves horror, fantasy and science fiction and is interested in writing for children, comic books, video games, and board games. She is an artist and looks after an elderly pet rabbit.

Anna Howard graduated from Roehampton in Drama in 2015, before embarking on her Creative Writing masters. Instead of a dissertation she wrote a one-hour play *Eclipse*, written half in poetry. *Fragments* is her first published story, inspired by a free-writing exercise. It is part of a longer exploration into human relationships in a post-apocalyptic world. Her work can be found on Instagram by the name of ASH_HARVEY_POETRY.

AUDREY JEAN [2015] is a visual artist and poet from France. Her visual compositions explore the relationship between poetry and the screen. She has studied an MSt in Film Aesthetics. She is inspired by philosophy and physical cosmology. Her favourite authors are Emily Dickinson and Philip Pullman. At time of publication, she is preparing to begin her PhD.

ELLIE KENNEDY is surprised to have her work published for the first time in *Purple Lights*. Her haiku series, *Holiday,* was inspired by real events that happened on many holidays she's been on, some of which her parents would rather not be reminded of, via poetry or otherwise.

JESSICA LACK [2016] is a lover of nonsense and a graduate of the Children's Literature master's programme at Roehampton. She has worked at HarperCollins Children's Books, Upstart Crow Literary, and Folio Literary Management. She has also published a short story with Book Smugglers Publishing.

HARRIET MAUKISCH is still in love with life, theatre and poetry. She would like to be more mysterious and thinks life's too short to find a matching pair of socks. *Worlds On A Shelf* is her first work to be published by Fincham Press. At the time of publication, she was completing an MA in Creative Writing at Roehampton.

SASKIA MEARS grew up in Norfolk and writes short things, usually at night. Despite the many strange situations she has witnessed as a bartender/pet owner/human being, her writing tends to focus on complicated relationships. *Mamihlapinatapai* and *Gabriel's Wharf* are her first published screenplay and flash fiction.

CORINNA MILLER is originally from Potomac, Maryland. She came to Roehampton to study Creative Writing and to escape the preposterous fees of American universities. *Cup of Coffee* is her first published piece. She would like to dedicate it to her father, who is not inspiration for any character in this story.

TOVA NASLUND is a Swedish writer, larper, and designer of role-playing games. Her story game *Acceptable Losses* is published in the *Seven Wonders* anthology (Pelgrane Press, 2016). She was raised in a town close to the Arctic Circle and blames the long winters for her grim and dark stories.

TESS O'HARA came straight to Roehampton from a California ministry school. When not working on her screenplay, *Single Teen Dad*, she enjoys wandering through central London. *Tate and Paul* was written following one such wander; the story won the editor's choice award at the 2016 Roehampton Creative Writing Day Competition soiree.

EMILY PARSONS [2014] is an Australian who ventured to London to study creative writing and philosophy. She is an avid explorer of the natural world and human nature, and aims to express those journeys on the page. She is interested in telling small stories, of ordinary people who are searching for meaning in their lives. She hopes to bring attention to her greatest love, Tasmania.

JACK PURKIS is an actor and writer. He graduated from The Royal Academy of Dramatic Art in 2013, before turning his attention to writing. In 2014, he wrote his first play, *Odd Jobs*, for Pentabus Theatre Company. *Late Summer in Shropshire* is inspired by his home county and is his first published short story.

JENNA REDAH [2016] started degrees in Architecture and Psychology before settling into Creative Writing with Drama, Theatre and Performance. *Yellow Velvet* is her first published piece, and at time of publication she is working on her debut novel, *Five and Bea*. When not writing, she enjoys drawing herself into Disney Princesses on Snapchat.

SAM ROSE [2015] wrote *2345 AD* completely by accident. While drafting a longer story, he was advised to remove everything except the introduction. What is left is the story in this anthology. Rose says this was one of his greatest learning experiences. At time of publication, he is working on his novel *The Extras* and hopes to begin a Creative Writing MA in 2016.

GEORGE ROSS is an active member of the National Youth Theatre of Great Britain. He also considers himself to be an accomplished Jedi master and Quidditch player. This is his first story to be published by Fincham Press.

LEONE ROSS [leoneross.com] is a writer, teacher and editor, and has been doing these things professionally for more than thirty years. She is a two-time, award-winning novelist, still seeking a home for her third progeny, *This One Sky Day*. She has spent the last 15 years publishing short stories all over the world. Her first collection, the Scott Prize shortlisted *Come Let Us Sing Anyway* will be published by Peepal Tree Press in 2017. Critic Maggie Gee has called her writing 'genius, surreal, mysterious and touching'. Ross has worked as a judge/consultant for several international writing competitions, including the 2015 Manchester Writing Competition, the 2016 SI Leeds Literary Prize and the Wimbledon Bookfest Short Story Competition. She is a Senior Lecturer in Creative Writing at Roehampton and member of the Fincham Press editorial board. *Purple Lights* is the third anthology she has edited for the Press. She thinks you should buy the other two as well: *The Trouble With Parallel Universes* (2014) and *Screams & Silences* (2015). She can be found on Twitter @leoneross.

AGNE SADAUNIKAITE [2015] regularly publishes poetry and snippets of fiction at sheepskates.wordpress.com. Her work is inspired by the randomness of nature and the ambiguity of the senses. The two poems in *Purple Lights* are her first published pieces of writing.

VICTORIA STEVENS lives with her four needy cats in a haunted house in the countryside, where she spends her time writing stories about love and death (in equal measure). Her debut novel *Don't Forget Me,* about love, loss and the art of moving on, will be published by FSG/Macmillan in 2017. She and her writing can be found at www.victoriastevenswrites.com.

VERA SUGAR [2014] is a London-based writer of poetry and fiction. Her background includes creative writing, journalism and history. She has had several works published on literary blogs, and is developing a career in publishing. Her novel excerpt, *How To Drink Coffee,* was inspired by her grandfather and father, although she has taken great care not to tell them so.

OMARI SWANSTON-JEFFERS [2015] is the writer-director and founder of Ol' Man Swanny Productions. After graduating with first class honours, he is now a rookie in the film industry. He has worked as a production runner, in front of the camera and gained a handful of production credits.

HANNAH VALLY is an American writer from Los Angeles, California. She graduated from Chapman University with a BFA in Creative Writing, and a minor in Art History. She generally writes fiction, but likes to take sabbaticals from fiction to write nonfiction pieces about her sabbaticals from writing fiction. She attended the University of Roehampton for one term in 2015.

KAROLINE MOEN VEMBRE [2014] is, at the time of publication, completing her MFA in Writing for Stage at the Royal Central School of Speech and Drama, and working with Antistrophe Theatre Company. She has had several plays staged, and in 2014 her play *Mørke* was part of the Malta International Theatre Festival. Her writing has been published by *Kår* magazine and by Fincham Press.

STEPH ELLIOT VICKERS is an East London native and writer of short fiction, narrative nonfiction and memoir. She has since moved away from the city, but can't stop writing about it. *Ridley Road* is her second short story to be published by Fincham Press. Her first, *Hark The Herald Angel*, won the editor's choice award at the 2011 Roehampton Creative Writing Day Competition.

RUFUS H.B. WILLIAMS was born in London in 1995. At time of publication, he is studying Creative Writing and Film at Roehampton University. *Moodle: My Portal To Hell*, which appears here, was also runner-up for the Roehampton Hopkins Prize 2016.

CLEO WREFORD [2015] lives by the South Coast with her dog, two degus and a large collection of eerie dolls. *Words*, which is her second story published by Fincham Press, popped into her head during a long train journey. She draws inspiration from Mark Z. Danielewski and late-night horror films.

9 7 8 0 9 9 2 8 5 8 1 3 1